S0-BEV-411

MASTERS
AND
JOHNSON
EXPLAINED

MASTERS
AND
JOHNSON
EXPLAINED

by **PLAYBOY** editor
NAT LEHRMAN

PLAYBOY PRESS

Copyright © 1970 by Nat Lehrman. All rights reserved.

Published simultaneously in the United States and Canada by Playboy Press, Chicago, Illinois. Printed in the United States of America. Library of Congress Catalog Card Number: 73-135532. First edition.

Man survives earthquakes, epidemics, the horrors of illness, and all the tortures of the soul, but the most tormenting tragedy at all times has been, is and will be the tragedy of the bedroom.
Tolstoy

The only thing we have to fear is fear itself.
Franklin D. Roosevelt

contents

PART 1 human sexual inadequacy

PART 2 human sexual response

PART 3 the psychotherapeutic background

FOREWORD

W. H. Masters and V. E. Johnson

Nat Lehrman has done a thoroughly professional job of melding highlights from both *Human Sexual Response* and *Human Sexual Inadequacy*. His abstractions of major portions of these texts provide clear pictures of problems of male and female sexual interaction. His translations have lost none of the original investigative authority in the process.

Human Sexual Inadequacy must be evaluated in depth by representatives of a variety of medical and behavioral disciplines and the pertinent material reproduced and applied clinically by multiple sources if there ever is to be generalized acceptance of the Reproductive Biology Research Foundation's therapeutic concepts and techniques. Critical professional evaluation of clinical content constitutes an important aspect of the Lehrman manual.

We are most grateful for the author's controlled, objective approach to handling the subject of human sexual function and dysfunction. This happens all too infrequently in our society.

St. Louis, July 1970

PREFACE

Mary S. Calderone

Coitus is one of the most extraordinary, the most complex and the least understood of all of the phenomena exhibited by the human animal. Certainly it is the least studied. True, the anatomist has provided us with knowledge of the structures involved, but where our similar structural knowledge of all the other parts of the body has been brought alive for us by numberless physiologists, biochemists, neurologists, pharmacologists, psychiatrists and ecologists, not so for coitus, whose investigators have been few and so suspect as usually to have had to remain anonymous. Our scientific institutions continue to distinguish the subject by their avoidance of it. Deep-seated sexual problems may be touched upon in the medical curriculum, usually in the department of psychiatry, but the medical student is practically never given instruction in the normal aspects of sexual life, and is rarely, if ever, given any orientation in the "normal abnormalities" of sexual behavior as he is bound to meet them in his practice.*

The above observations were made in 1964. In 1966 the epoch-making 11-year studies of Masters and Johnson reported in their *Human Sexual Response,* for the first time in history, provided a solid base for understanding coitus in physiological functioning rather than merely in anatomy. Since 1968 the Center for the Study of Sex Education in Medicine, under the direction of Dr. Harold I. Lief of the University of Pennsylvania Medical School, has provided

---

*From preface by Mary S. Calderone to *Manual of Contraceptive Practice,* edited by M. S. Calderone, Baltimore, The Williams and Wilkins Co., 1964.

permanent liaison for training and orientation in human sexuality with faculties of close to 100 medical schools. In 1970, with the publication of the present landmark volume on *Human Sexual Inadequacy,* by Masters and Johnson, sexual problems in marriage are classified and described as to their psychosocial as well as biophysical natures, origins and therapies. Thus, in a span of only five years, society has been given the means by which men and women might attain a degree of sexual fulfillment and enrichment in their personal married lives that, at this moment, cannot yet be measured nor perhaps even imagined by many married couples, whether of that 50 percent who identify themselves as having sexual problems or of that 50 percent who consider themselves to be free of such.

For the more coitus is understood, the more it stands as extraordinary, if only because no other human function resembles it. It is not necessary to life; yet few people wish to live without it. It can give infinite variety, excitement and color to a relationship, but these very qualities can wither or grow stale when feverishly sought for themselves alone. Desire for it is self-renewing—yet its accomplishment may give little satisfaction, because, as indicated by Masters and Johnson, it can so easily be deflected by a host of influences that may begin to bear in on the individual from his earliest infancy. Unlike other bodily functions, as Masters and Johnson point out, its psychosocial component bears so heavily on it that it may vary greatly in intensity and enjoyment between individuals as well as from occasion to occasion in the same individual. Depending on the individual, ignorance about it, whether circumstantial or studiously maintained because of religious or puritanical attitudes, may result in failure or stultifying boredom with it, whereas knowledge about it that dispels its mysteries may actually serve to enhance not only its performance but its wonderments.

For me, personally, the three most meaningful messages of the book are the importance placed on the marital relationship, the beauty of full sexual experience for people over 50, and the gate it unlocks to free us from the pernicious trap that had been constructed, with all good intentions, of course, by the long and still-continuing line of so-called marriage manuals beginning with Van der Velde's. It is clear that the term *foreplay* and the emphasis on techniques and performance in these manuals have actually served to create problems. What Masters and Johnson have developed indicates a much needed evolution away from coitus dominated by a stereotyped male drive to orgasm as fast as possible, toward enhanced enjoyment by both male and female of the arousal phase in and for itself, rather than merely as the inevitable prelude to orgasm.

With new understanding developed of the almost unlimited possibilities for sensed pleasure in one's own body, both man and woman during the arousal phase can learn what it is to "experience" each other—she to savor to the full, and perhaps for the first time, the sensation of penile containment; he the sensation of being contained. When full value is given to the validity of the arousal or excitement phase in and of itself, then the inhibitory effects of compulsiveness to performance in orgasm become minimized—and the capacity for orgasm with which we are all endowed can be released.

Different societies throughout history, and even different groups within those societies, have given different values to coitus—ranging from obsessive exploitation or even worship of it, on the one hand, to equally obsessive attempts at grim repression of it, on the other. We see this entire range of attitudes around us in our society this very day—with a range of sexual misery and dissatisfaction to correspond. Our era is so fortunate in these two warmly insightful and inspired scientists that interpretation to the general public of the meanings and implications of their efforts is of great importance to accomplish as swiftly as possible. This is the intent of the present book, thoughtfully written and compiled by Nat Lehrman.

New York City, July 1970

To Bill Masters and Gini Johnson for their encouragement, assistance and friendship; to Mary Calderone, who read parts of the text and offered invaluable advice; to Pat Prince, who prepared the manuscript with unfailingly smiling diligence; and not least of all, to Kaz, Jerry and Cindy, whose love, patience and support made it possible to produce this book during evenings and weekends that rightfully belonged to them. Thank you.

N. L.

INTRODUCTION

Nat Lehrman

Why is this book necessary? Alex Comfort, writing in the *New Scientist,* offers some insight into why Masters and Johnson require explanation: " 'The complainee in the marital unit contending with an established pattern of premature ejaculation usually is the female partner'—in other words, if the man comes too quickly, it is usually the wife who grumbles. Masters and Johnson adopted the same style—mistakenly, I think—in their first book: Not because they cannot write decent English, but because by writing in gobbledygook, they hope to insure that people like . . . Spiro Agnew will be unable to understand their work and shut it down."

I think Comfort is correct, but there are other reasons why scientists like Masters and Johnson write the way they do. First, they are professionals who want to impart their discoveries *first* to their peers—the physicians, psychotherapists, clergymen and other counselors to whom people bring sexual problems. These are "pros" with advanced education; they *should* be able to comprehend the ideas in a text even though not plainly expressed. Moreover, William Masters, who expresses himself with more attention to concision than to grace, and Virginia Johnson, vice versa, do not want to devote the time that is necessary to produce polished writing. They are scientists and they feel their time is best spent in the lab, not at the typewriter. (In Masters' specific case, it must be remembered, too, that he is a physician, and anyone who expects readable writing from a doctor is reminded to look carefully at his next prescription. Some unkind critics have suggested that *Human Sexual Response* reads like a 366-page prescription—in Latin, yet.) *Human Sexual Inadequacy*, lacking the Latinate medical mumbo jumbo that handicapped their first book, is much more readable but is still not something to take along while bouncing home on the 5:30 bus.

Masters and Johnson encourage others to explain their writing because they feel that the information contained in their two volumes, once absorbed by specialists, ought to be disseminated to as broad a segment of the general public as possible. There are many causes, they believe, of sexual unhappiness, but one of the most pervasive is ignorance. They want people who either can't or won't grapple with a medical text to understand that human sexual dysfunction is not only fixable but is more common than anyone suffering from it will allow himself to believe. Apart from this proclamation of hope for sexually distressed individuals, there's also a message for the effectively functioning person as well. If ignorance is one of the greatest *causes* of sexual failure, then it follows that the broadcast of factually accurate information should serve a *preventive* function.

That's why this book is necessary.

Once having answered the above question, the next one is "Why me?" I'm employed full time as an editor at PLAYBOY (my basic responsibilities: editing *The Playboy Advisor, The Playboy Forum*, administering The Playboy Foundation, and obtaining articles about human behavior), and the task of putting this book together had to be done in my spare time. But this was a burden I was glad to undergo because Masters and Johnson asked me to do it. I was in their offices during the early part of 1970, looking at the first-draft manuscript of *Human Sexual Inadequacy*, so that I could offer some advice about its editing. I argued that the importance of their ideas merited a more meticulous job of writing than they had up to that time been willing to do. They demurred, for reasons I've already explained. But Dr. Masters said, "We agree that a simplified version of this material should reach the public. Why don't *you* do it after the book is published?"

To have refused the privilege of editing an authorized popularization of the work of these two pioneering geniuses would have been tantamount, in my opinion, to turning down a like opportunity to collaborate with Freud or Kinsey. For there's no question in my mind that Masters and Johnson are in the same trail-blazing swath of the father of psychiatry and the patriarch of sex research. Just note a *few* of their major accomplishments:

¶Taking sex off the drawing board and moving it into the lab

¶Conclusively removing the clitoral-vaginal orgasm controversy from the bedroom

¶Definitively destroying myths about the presumed lack of effectiveness of the small penis

¶Discovering that sex and old age are not mutually exclusive

¶Chalking up an unprecedented 80-percent cure rate among people suffering from various kinds of sexual inadequacy

There are too many shattered precedents to mention. One that strikes me as especially significant is the fact that they are the first important sex researchers who truly see sex from the point of view of *both* the male and the female. They don't, like the orthodox Freudians, regard the woman as a supplement to the man, whose sexual needs derive from his; and they don't, like the sex-manualists of the last two generations (beginning with Van der Velde), over-react in the other direction, decreeing that the man should serve as an adoring and self-effacing tool to help stimulate the underprivileged female's responses. No. Masters and Johnson argue that male and female sexual response are very much alike. Accordingly, in none of their therapy is one sex required to pay reparations to the other (even though *individuals* of either sex might sometimes be asked to make special concessions.) This is an important step in restoring a balance to sexual relations. Up to now, one sex or the other has been a sex object: the woman in the Victorian ethos and the man in the neoromanticism ushered in by Van der Velde. In the Masters and Johnson system neither sex uses the other; it is possible to stimulate a partner only if you are stimulating yourself, just as you can truly satisfy yourself only if you have satisfied your partner.

The information in this book has been laid out chronologically backward, with the newest material up front. Part 3 *(The Psychotherapeutic Background)* presents concepts that precede Masters and Johnson, but which help provide an understanding of where they've come from and where they're going. Morton Hunt's chapter (7) on behavior therapy is a simplified explanation of a relatively new form of psychotherapy that's crucial to the work done by Masters and Johnson. Chapters 5 and 6 contain psychoanalytic interpretations of impotence and frigidity.

Part 2 *(Human Sexual Response)* contains *The Playboy Interview* with Masters and Johnson (chapter 4). They have described this interview as the best they've ever given and Dr. Alan Guttmacher (the birth-control crusader) has suggested it be included as an appendix to future editions of *Human Sexual Response*. In this interview, the authors explain all the major concepts of their first book in an easily understood conversational format. Part 2 also includes a selection of *Playboy Advisor* letters and answers (chapter 3), all of them dealing with material related to *Human Sexual Response*.

Masters and Johnson's newest work, *Human Sexual Inadequacy*, is dealt with in detail in Part 1. The first chapter is an interpretation I've written of that book, and chapter 2 is an edited transcript of a 12-hour press conference held by Masters and Johnson the week their book was published. It contains a number of fascinating insights about *Human Sexual Inadequacy* by its authors that were not published in the book or elsewhere.

I had hoped to write a short biography of Masters and Johnson for inclusion in this book, but I despaired of trying to capture the complex interaction of their wholly different yet complementary personalities in the time and space available. Someday, perhaps they'll honor me by letting me write a complete biography of them. Meanwhile, the sketchy insights afforded by *The Playboy Interview* (chapter 4) are offered as a substitute.

But I do want to mention one incident in our acquaintanceship that exquisitely illustrates a side of their character that is not well enough known. I first met them in the fall of 1967 at a conference in New York and took that occasion to offer them the hospitality of our offices in Chicago, only a short trip from their headquarters in St. Louis.

We were soon back in our respective cities and on the phone, making arrangements—which is an inadequate word to explain what was going on. Part of their visit to Chicago was to include a meeting with my boss, Hugh M. Hefner; and the finding of mutually agreeable dates and the making of mutually agreeable arrangements for three such busy people as these would have taxed the abilities of the State Department's chief protocol officer. I don't have any talent in that direction, but miraculously a date was finally set.

Meanwhile, I mentioned the upcoming visit to one of my editorial associates. He said, "Have you seen this month's *Annie Fanny*?" *Annie Fanny,* for the uninitiated, is an irregular PLAYBOY feature that is masterminded by satirist Harvey Kurtzman (founding editor of *Mad*) and which, in a sexy and irreverent way, takes on the major issues of our time in cartoon format.

"No," I told my associate. "I haven't seen *Annie.* Who's she doing this month?"

"You'd better look," said my concerned colleague.

Undoubtedly, the readers of this introduction have figured out quicker than I did that Kurtzman had decided to take on sex in the laboratory for the January issue of 1968. I looked at one of the advance copies, and there was this photographic likeness of Dr. Masters, only looking sinister and insane. The mad scientist's name, ha-ha, was Dr. Master. His female associate didn't look *exactly* like Mrs. Johnson, but it wasn't because the cartoonist hadn't tried; as a gross caricature, it would do fine.

I won't recount the plot here; suffice it to say that Annie (who is a large-boobed and pretty version of Little Orphan Annie) and an equally well-endowed friend, Wanda Home-free, bounce through a succession of adventures until the strip concludes (climaxes, I guess) with the two heroines about to jump into bed with a sex machine fabricated by guess who.

I nearly died. Masters and Johnson were due in about a week, and what was I to do? Call them and risk blowing the visit? Sit tight and hope they wouldn't see *Annie Fanny*?

Stop the issue from being distributed until after the visit? Walk into the elevator shaft?

An Englishman once said, "When in doubt, do nothing." I was never in more doubt in my life; so I just sat tight and hoped the gods would guide me through this one.

Well, one of the gods picked up an advance copy of the magazine and sent it to Masters and Johnson. They received it during a period when *every*one was doing satires of them (including two book-length jobs). This god must have had more insight into their characters than I, because I'd have assumed they'd blow their stacks.

They didn't. But even more significantly, Virginia Johnson had the kindness, just a couple of days before she and Dr. Masters were due to arrive in Chicago, to call me and tell me they'd seen the *Annie Fanny* satire and that *I* shouldn't worry about it.

That's the kind of people they are.

Chicago, July 1970

Part 1

HUMAN SEXUAL INADEQUACY

1

A REPORT ON HUMAN SEXUAL INADEQUACY

This chapter represents a short, explanatory tour through the key concepts in Masters and Johnson's clinical report on the psychology of sex and the treatment of sexual problems in marriage. Intended as a supplement rather than as a substitute for a reading of the text, it should help the reader put the subtle and complex concepts of the work into perspective. Anyone truly wishing to appreciate the momentously new and important theories of Human Sexual Inadequacy *should take the time to make an extended visit with that book.*

THE PATIENTS

Fifty percent of all marriages in this country are beset with some form of sexual inadequacy, ranging from serious problems (e.g., impotence, frigidity, premature ejaculation) to lesser complaints such as unequal levels of sexual response. This is the opinion of William H. Masters and Virginia E. Johnson, director and associate director of the Reproductive Biology Research Foundation, a clinic whose aim is to improve the quality of some of these marriages, and ultimately to train other therapists to treat the rest.

And make no mistake about it—the foundation treats *marriages*, not only the sexual component thereof. A sexual distress does not develop in a vacuum; rather, it reflects the accumulation of the partners' backgrounds and personalities combined with their marital interaction. If a male is impotent, or a wife nonorgasmic, the other partner cannot claim to be "uninvolved": More than any other kind of intercourse, the sexual kind represents a mutual feedback situation. In fact, in many cases of sexual distress, the partner will have a complementary sexual difficulty: 44 percent of all couples who came to the foundation for treatment suffered from such dual dysfunctions.

The total number of patients treated by the foundation during the period 1959–1969 (11 years, during which records were kept for analysis in *Human Sexual Inadequacy*) was 790. As just mentioned, some of these represent both sides of a marriage (of 510 couples, 223 had dual sexual distresses, making a total of 446 patients in this category whose treatment was statistically recorded); others represent just the suffering half (287—the ratio here was 60 male distresses to 40 female). There were 54 unmarried males and three single women.

What are the patients like? Mostly American, some Canadian; about 12 percent living right in St. Louis, where the therapy is administered. Socially, the patients are described as middle class and above, with 72.7 percent having had some higher education.

In this period of concern for the underprivileged, the question occurs: Why so many people with financial and educational privileges? Don't "hard hats" ever suffer from soft penises? At first glance, one might attribute the high-income distribution to the ample fee charged by the foundation, plus the cost of travel and living in a St. Louis hotel for two weeks. The charge is $2500 per unit (the "unit" is the focus of treatment—it might be a single-person unit or a marital unit). But the cost doesn't explain everything, because no fee was charged patients during the period 1959–1964, while the program was being stabilized, and since then only 50 percent of the patients have paid a full fee. Twenty-five percent were treated free, and the remaining 25 percent were charged cost ($1250) or less.

Another possible explanation for the dearth of lower-stratum patients is that the psychiatrists and other counselors who refer patients to the St. Louis clinic do not deal with this kind of client. Still another explanation arises from the fact that the double sexual standard is stronger among people of low education than among the middle class. This would account for women in the lower group not *expecting* to have orgasms and for men fearing to report impotence to an outsider because of the tremendous loss of *machismo* it represents. Moreover, among such men, premature ejaculation is probably not considered a dysfunction, but rather the normal mode of operation.

A final explanation is that members of the lower stratum either do not experience or do not recognize as such the problems suffered by better-educated, higher-income men and women. Masters and Johnson, while mentioning all these possibilities, state that they do not yet have the data even to speculate on any of them.

Whatever stratum they represent, all the patients must be screened by a "referral authority." This means they must have undergone treatment—or at least an interview—by a physician, clergyman, psychiatrist, psychologist, social worker or marriage counselor. In many cases, the two-week rapid-treatment program at the foundation is an integral part of a larger regimen of therapy administered elsewhere. For example, an individual diagnosed as neurotic may be undergoing a five-year course in psychoanalysis back home. There is no reason why he cannot interrupt it temporarily for a rapid-treatment reversal of his sexual-dysfunction symptoms; in fact, this may help speed his general recovery. On the other hand, Masters and Johnson point out that sexual dysfunction is not *always* a symptom of a psychiatric problem; it is often caused by little more than pervasive ignorance, both of sexual physiology and of human relations.

Some exceptions to the foundation screening rules: They will not accept acute psychotics, and they will accept physicians and clinical psychologists who refer themselves (there were 89 couples in the program in which either the husband or wife or both had had medical training).

THE DYSFUNCTIONS

Beyond the interaction between partners that is essential to sexual performance, there is within the individual a crucial interaction between the mind and the body. If, for some reason, the body does not operate effectively—for example, the destruction of certain neurological functions could prevent a man from having an erection—then the dysfunction is described as physiological. But very few of the cases seen at the foundation were in this class. Most often, there occurs a short circuit between the mental signals and the physical function that they operate, and the greatest over-all cause of this malfunction is *fear*.

As we shall see within the descriptions of the individual dysfunctions, fear makes a person overly conscious of what he or she is doing; in sex (as in some other physical activities), the more self-conscious we become about our physiological function, the less likely is it that the function will perform as expected. Think of the professional golf player who is poised to make a six-foot putt, something he has done successfully many times in his life. But a crowd is watching this time, and big money is at stake. What may happen is that the golfer suddenly becomes conscious of what he is doing and fearful that he may not be able to do it; instead of allowing his body to perform as it always has in this situation, directed by brain signals which form a smooth complement with his motor functions, he now brings in a portion of his mind that is not ordinarily part of this teamwork. This intrusion interferes with the golfer's accustomed rhythm and results in a flubbed shot—and the danger, for future shots, particularly if the golfer tends to lack confidence, that the memory of the failure will introduce new failures.

The foundation's goal is to take patients who have become habituated to viewing sex at this same level of mental removal—and to restore their performance to its natural rhythm.

IMPOTENCE: The model of a fear-operated sexual syndrome is male impotence, which can be defined as the male's inability to perform intercourse due to the failure of his penis to become and/or remain erect. (The word derives from Latin and means literally "without power.") Many psychiatrists classify premature ejaculation and ejaculatory incompetence (both discussed later in this chapter) as forms of impotence, but Masters and Johnson confine their classification solely to problems of erective inadequacy. Within this category, however, they have subclassified two separate forms: *primary* and *secondary*.

PRIMARY IMPOTENCE: This describes a man who has, from the first time he has tried, *never* been able to achieve or maintain an erection of sufficient quality to perform sexual intercourse. This is a relatively rare affliction: Only 32 males were treated for it during the clinic's 11-year investigative program. Twenty-one of these men were unmarried; of the 11 married men, the periods of marital celibacy ranged from seven months to 18 years.

Masters and Johnson believe that the underlying cause of most cases of primary impotence is a complex interaction of a traumatic first attempt at intercourse with a background dominated by destructively negative sexual attitudes. The authors stress, however, that the same set of circumstances will not affect two different men in the same way: One may in fact overcome the trauma and the debilitating background to go on to enjoy a pleasurable sex life, while the other may never succeed in having intercourse. By the same token, some men whose backgrounds do not seem to predispose toward impotence fail the first time for one of any number of reasons and never recover from the ego-destructive shock.

Among the specific causes isolated by Masters and Johnson were untoward maternal influences, a severely restrictive religious background, homosexual involvement and loss of personal esteem resulting from a prostitute experience.

Maternal Influence: In all three cases described as maternal, the young man slept in his mother's bedroom before, during and after puberty. One patient reported waking up to find his mother manipulating his penis; another described sleeping with his nude mother; the third reported that his mother always washed his genitals while bathing him and assured him "no other girl will be able to please you as mother does." (Philip Roth's fictional portrayal of a mother who proudly refers to her son's penis as "that little thing" goes in the other direction, perhaps, but the message about smother-loving mothers remains the same. Portnoy's complaint, of course, was impotence.) These are extreme examples of a wide range of seductive mother-son behavior, not all of them so clearly sexual, that can interfere with a man's adult sexual adjustment. Therapy of the sexual problem would not replace but would tend to reinforce needed additional psychotherapy.

Religious Orthodoxy: Six men were raised in ultraorthodox religious environments (two Jewish, four Catholic), and all approached their wedding nights crippled in advance by ignorance, anxiety and fear. In five of the six cases, the wife was as misinformed and tense as the husband, which merely added to his problem. Masters and Johnson write:

> When premarital sexual expression has been restricted to handholding, the first fumbling, bumbling, theologically and legally acceptable attempts at sexual connection are often unsuccessful. This psychosocial diversion of the natural biophysical process may evolve into the disastrous combination of a severely shredded male ego further traumatized by the unreasonable, but so understandable, female partner's virginally blind insistence that he *"do something."* This semihysterical supplication first whispered, then suggested, eventually demanded, and finally, screamed, *"Do something,"* renders the equally virginal and equally traumatized male incapable not only of effective sexual function but also of situational comprehension. His wife's emotional importuning creates such a concept of frustration, failure and loss of masculine stature that the marital unit's frequently repeated, obviously frantic attempts at sexual connection usually are doomed to failure.
>
> Severe religious orthodoxy may indoctrinate the teenager with the concept that any form of overt sexual activity prior to marriage not only is totally unacceptable but is personally destructive, demoralizing, degrading, dehumanizing and injurious to one's physical and/or mental health.[1]

Homosexual Involvement: Six of the 32 primarily impotent men had been involved in homosexual affairs of varying duration during their early and middle teens. Although all these men expressed a desire to be able to function heterosexually, the conflicts over their earlier relationships were thought to contribute to their failure at intercourse with a woman.

Prostitute Experience: Four of the impotent males had none of the negative background of the other cases, but were so repelled by the squalor, dehumanization and ugliness of their first experience with a prostitute that they could not function sexually then or thereafter. In three of the cases, the young men's natural anxieties at being in an unfamiliar social environment were compounded by whores with hearts of cement who made fun of them at crucial moments; in the fourth case, the young man was fifth in line during a gang-shag, and he was simply overwhelmed by the pressure to perform, not only from the prostitute but from his sated, impatient and unsympathetic companions.

Masters and Johnson classified these common causes of primary impotence simply for ease of description; the problem in any individual is complex and the causes multiple. Once the element of fear, shared by all, is discounted, it is difficult to trace any other factors that can be identified as common—with the exception that in all cases, there is an unusual and unexplained sensitivity in a particular male to unidentified psychological influences. This male can be expected to have a negative value system about sex, deeply inculcated in his formative years, and his sensitivity can be expected to act as a magnifier of an initial failure, blowing it up into an obsessive and self-destructive concern for future performance. As soon as the panicked male asks himself, after he fails the first time, "Will I fail next time?" he has already answered his question. Fears that one will not be able to perform sexually inevitably act as self-fulfilling prophecies.

Although the physiological mechanisms of secondary and primary impotence are identical, the psychological causes and concerns can be quite dissimilar.

SECONDARY IMPOTENCE: The man suffering from primary impotence has never succeeded in having intercourse; in secondary impotence, the man has succeeded at least once, maybe several—or several hundred—times, over a period of decades; but then he fails on a particular occasion. His failure may be due to one or a combination of many common causes. He may be fatigued, or distracted by other matters, or he may feel hostile to his partner. He may be ill or under the influence of drugs or alcohol. Any of these can inhibit sexual performance temporarily with no predictable after-effects. Whatever it is, some factor has intruded on the inter-action between his body and that part of his mind that supplies sexual signals. If he understands the nature of the intrusion and is confident of his sexual ability, if he discounts the experience as a bum trip and forgets about it, he may never have potency problems. But if he lets it prey on his mind, increasing his apprehension about future performances and allowing his manhood to be threatened—a ripe possibility in a society that demands that the responsibility for sexual success rest with the male—then his fears will be realized. Over and over again. When his failure rate approaches or moves beyond 25 percent of his sexual opportunities, he is defined as secondarily impotent.

In many cases of secondary impotence, though a specific agent may trigger the failure, there are often underlying causes—perhaps building up over a period of years—that help perpetuate it. Of 213 secondarily impotent males treated at the foundation, Masters and Johnson classified 63 cases as being due to premature ejaculation; 35, alcohol consumption; 23, maternal or paternal dominance; 26, religious orthodoxy; 21, homosexual conflict; 27, inadequate counseling; and 7, physiological. (The remaining 11 were in miscellaneous categories.)

Premature Ejaculation: The premature ejaculator typically has his orgasm before his partner can have hers, and he leaves her in a state of frustration. In most married cases, the wife has complained about this, gently at first, then, over the years (10 to 20), accusingly, demandingly and finally contemptuously. The frequently uncomprehending male eventually gets the message that he's not man enough to satisfy his wife, and he attempts all the tried and true remedies to improve his performance. He bites his lips, thinks of his work, plans the next day's activities, constricts his rectal sphincters and counts backward. In short, he does his best to take his mind *off* his sexual excitement, and indeed, should his wife become stimulated and begin thrusting, he frantically attempts to escape from her demands and from the sensation of vaginal containment which makes him feel he is losing control. Eventually, his assiduous efforts to dull his sexual sensibilities and to ignore his wife's responsiveness become successful. In fact, so successful that he becomes impotent. The turning point will often occur on some occasion when the husband, for one reason or another, is not up to a sexual encounter, but the wife will insist on one. He'll fail to have an erection, and then the normal chain of fear set into motion by this event will be hastened along by his sensitivity to his wife's previously expressed contempt for his lack of masculinity.

Alcohol Consumption: The difference between secondary impotence caused by premature ejaculation and by alcohol is the difference between a long, steady attrition of the male ego and a single-occasion trauma. The crucial incident will typically occur in the life of an educated, middle-aged man of moderately high income, who is subject to a great deal of social and psychological tension and responds to it by convivial boozing. On a Saturday night, he'll go to a party with his wife, drink heavily (to her annoyance), have a nightcap upon his return and decide to play Tarzan in bed to his wife's Jane. But, as was known even in Shakespeare's time, tippling "provokes the desire but takes away the performance" (alcohol, after all, is a depressant). So Tarzan slides down the vine—limply—and, before he can figure out why, falls asleep.

Sunday is an uneventful day, during which he suffers uneasy feelings about the night before, but he makes no real attempt to understand why. He has enough unconscious sense of what happened, however, to beat his wife to bed that night, so that he'll not be put to the test.

On Monday, he spends a troublesome day, focusing a little more clearly now on his weekend failure and intermittently vowing to test himself that night. In the typical case, he doesn't.

By Tuesday, however, he'll have become preoccupied with proving his potency. He stops off for a couple of spine-stiffening drinks (the association perhaps not entirely unconscious) and arrives to the arms of a wife who has by now gotten over her irritation with her husband's weekend behavior. But, once in bed, he quickly notices that his erection doesn't have its usual zip, and he panics. He tries desperately to get the old erective quality back, but the more he dwells on it, the further from happening will it be. At the same time, his wife tries resolutely to help, but her compassion merely makes him feel more inadequate, because it highlights his incapacity to do the job when it needs to be done.

Thus, typically, the second bout of alcohol-induced impotence occurs 72 hours after the first. Thereafter, his sexual prowess will fluctuate; sometimes, he'll do the job, sometimes not, but he'll always be conscious of his occasional failures, and he'll consider going to bed more of a challenge than an opportunity. Soon, he'll begin to blame his age, and he'll start avoiding intercourse altogether. At first, his wife will push for additional sexual expression, to prove to herself that she has not lost her attractiveness, but then she'll begin avoiding contact, for fear of pressuring her husband (and his awareness of her thoughtfulness will be the greatest kind of pressure). Ultimately, communication breaks down throughout the relationship, until the marriage itself is seriously threatened.

Parental Imbalance: In cases of parental imbalance, the male goes through life with a sense of masculinity that is constantly threatened. An overprotective mother (and correspondingly passive or absent father) leaves the boy with no male to identify with. At the opposite extreme, an overbearing father may cause the son to develop *too* strong an image of masculinity, one that is nearly impossible to live up to. This type of male constantly must test his masculinity, and, therefore, failure to perform sexually—the ultimate test in our culture—can be absolutely overwhelming. Via the fear syndrome already described, one failure will almost inevitably lead to a pattern of failure.

Religious Orthodoxy: The cases of primary and secondary impotence caused by religious orthodoxy are similar—except that in the latter, there was at least one successful sexual encounter. The religions of these 26 secondarily impotent men were Jewish (6), Catholic (11) and Protestant (4). There were also five mixed marriages in this group.

In the previously described cases of secondary impotence, the symptoms do not usually begin to appear until long after the man's initial sexual encounter. In cases influenced by a rigid religious background, failure, if not happening the very first time, occurs soon thereafter, with the underlying cause a deeply inculcated belief that sex has no honorable place in life. Thus, taken out of its natural context, sex for such men and women—even those who do not develop major dysfunctions—can, according to the authors, be characterized as "stylized, unimaginative, depersonalized, and indeed productive only of biological reproduction." [2]

Homosexual Involvement: Typically, the secondarily impotent male in this category is introduced to homosexual experience during his teens by an older person, and by the time the relationship is over, he is convinced of his permanent homosexual orientation. His masturbatory fantasies revolve around high school athletic heroes, and his heterosexual dating pattern is sporadic. When he does relate to a girl, it is generally as a "big brother." In college, his dating, though more frequent, is often used as a subterfuge to conceal his homosexual interests or to protect him*self* from his real interest in men.

When these men marry, it is often because they believe this will reverse their preference for males; more often, their marriages are purely for social, financial or professional reasons. Their sexual decline in marriage generally follows one of two patterns: Most frequently, the male's fears are well defined during the initial stage of the relationship, and his inadequacy surfaces early. In another well-established pattern, the man reports no difficulties until much later in the marriage, when, for reasons not clearly understood, his interest in males—usually teenagers—revives. The husband tries to live a double life, but his attention to his wife declines. She notices this loss of interest and begins to pressure him, which leads to an episode of failure and then—his heterosexual commitment not being very dedicated in the first place—a pattern of failure.

Inadequate Counseling: Frequently, the advice of an incompetent therapist is destructive to the potency of an insecure male. Several of the men listed in this category had been erroneously told by a therapist that their condition was caused by aging (see the section on "Sex and Aging" in this chapter). Others were told that their symptoms were caused by adultery or by a previous homosexual experience or by masturbation in adulthood. Although none of these factors can cause impotence, such a suggestion by an authority figure can serve not only to worsen an existing condition but actually to initiate a dysfunction where none existed before.

Physiological Causes: Although impotence caused by a physical condition is relatively rare, virtually any illness that seriously reduces the body's metabolic efficiency can be a background factor in an impotence case. Masters and Johnson list 66 medical conditions that have been associated with erective failure, but they stress that a *direct* cause and effect, or biophysical link, between a physiological condition and loss of potency is infrequent. The notable exception is diabetes, which many medical experts believe is neurologically linked to impotence. Masters and Johnson feel that, in spite of the high correlation between diabetes and erective inadequacy, present studies on the subject are inconclusive, and they suspect that other causes may combine with the onset of a diabetic condition to influence the male's loss of erective function. They hasten to add that their research in this area is still incomplete.

The authors conclude this section by emphasizing the rarity of a physical cause and effect in impotence:

> Understandably, for many years the pattern of the human male has been to blame sexual dysfunction on specific physical distresses. Every sexually inadequate male lunges toward any potential physical excuse for sexual malfunction. From point of view of ego support, would that it could be true. A cast for a leg or a sling for an arm provides socially acceptable evidence of physical dysfunction of these extremities. Unfortunately the psychosocial causes of perpetual penile flaccidity cannot be explained or excused by devices for mechanical support.[9]

PREMATURE EJACULATION: Of all the sexual dysfunctions dealt with in *Human Sexual Inadequacy,* premature ejaculation is least susceptible to a scientific definition. The premature ejaculator can be the man who ejaculates before penetrating the vagina, or immediately upon entering, or well after penetration but before his partner has been satisfied (to her, what is premature may be plenty mature to another woman who is capable of quicker response). Many of the existing definitions rely on an arbitrary period of time—i.e., if a man beats, let's say, one minute on a stop watch, he's premature. Masters and Johnson reject this concept, pointing out that with adequate precoital stimulation, many women can be satisfied in this period of time, meaning *their* men are not premature (though they might be with other women). Masters and Johnson's definition, accordingly, is purely relative: If a man cannot bring his female partner to orgasm during intercourse on at least 50 percent of his opportunities—regardless of his timing—then he's a premature ejaculator. But what happens if the female is nonorgasmic for reasons not related to her partner's control? Then, says Dr. Masters, their definition is "shot full of holes." In actuality, the question of prematurity is mostly

related to the male *attitude* toward control of his ejaculation
—i.e., does he *want* to satisfy his partner?

Lack of control is not regarded as a problem by many
men—particularly in the lower educational strata—because
they're not concerned whether they satisfy their female
partners or not. And the partners don't complain, because
they usually have learned little about female sexual response
and frequently care less.

This sexual dysfunction is one of the few that is not caused
by a pattern of fear. For men born in the 1920s, whose first
sexual exposure tended to be with a prostitute, the rapid-fire
demands of these women conditioned the young customer
to continue ejaculating rapidly in future sexual encounters.
Men who were born somewhat later often had their first
sexual encounter in the back seat of a car, at a drive-in
movie or at a quickie motel. Here, too, a couple or three
"slam-bam-thank-you-ma'am" exposures were sufficient to
condition the susceptible young male to a lifetime of rapid
ejaculation. Yet another conditioning pattern involves the
teenage sexplay technique of rubbing clothed bodies together
until male orgasm is reached (colloquially called "dry
humping"). The sole concern here is to relieve the male of
his sex tension (so that he can avoid a painful swelling of
the testicles), but no regard is given to the high level of
frustration in which the female is left. This attitude carries
over into later life. The authors speculate, finally, that the
withdrawal technique—in which the male withdraws his
penis from his partner's vagina just before ejaculating—is
another cause, because it does not require the male to learn
ejaculatory control. The man, having protected his partner
from pregnancy with this method, congratulates himself and
tends to forget about her unfulfilled sexual tensions.

Generally, complaints of premature ejaculation are not
taken to the foundation until five to 20 years of marriage
have passed. Prior to that, the wife may have insisted on
professional guidance for herself or her husband, or she may
have tried to find sexual release with another partner, male
or female. Many home remedies are tried, such as an enforced
regime of not touching the male genitals during sexual foreplay; then, when the woman's sexual tension is very high,
he'll plunge in and cause a pathetic interaction: She will be

thrusting desperately to get some satisfaction before he ejaculates, and he will just as desperately be trying to distract himself—by thinking of unrelated matters—in order to keep from ejaculating. This self-defeating interplay, frustrating to both, because the highly excited woman forces the male to ejaculate while he is actually suppressing his enjoyment in order not to, finally leads the couple to avoid sex. Nothing, of course, will make the premature ejaculator ejaculate more prematurely than long periods of continence between sex exposures. And so the problem is compounded. As described earlier ("Secondary Impotence"), in this situation a shrewish wife can easily provoke erective problems in her husband if she harps often enough on his incapacity to do the job.

As can be seen by the examples given, the underlying cause of premature ejaculation is a pervasive social attitude that female sexual fulfillment is not on a par either in need, frequency or intensity with that of the male.

EJACULATORY INCOMPETENCE: The name of this dysfunction, chosen by Dr. Masters for its utility to the medical profession, is perhaps misleading. The "incompetent ejaculator" is in truth a nonejaculator (psychoanalysts call him a "retarded ejaculator"). He doesn't perform the job badly or "incompetently" (or even tardily); he performs it not at all. He cannot ejaculate while his penis is contained in the vagina. This is a relatively rare affliction—only 17 males were seen in therapy during 11 years—and it is precisely the opposite of premature ejaculation. The small clinical sample makes it difficult to sort out the causes of this dysfunction. In some cases, the male experiences this inability beginning with his first sexual encounter with his wife; in others, the male can ejaculate either with a nonmarital female partner or with a homosexual partner, but not with his wife; and in some cases, the male may be normal for a long period of time, until a traumatic experience causes him to lose his ejaculatory ability. The case histories cite one patient who lost his ejaculatory competence because of trauma relating to the alleged uncleanliness of the vagina; another male was frightened during masturbation as a youth; a third was jealous of a previous experience had by a supposedly virginal wife; three men simply found their wives distasteful and wished to reject them. There are also examples of pregnancy fear and trauma relating to birth-control attempts, to adultery by the wife, and to children surprising the parents during the sex act. In all these cases, for one reason or another, the male wishes, on a conscious or unconscious level, to withhold his ejaculate.

Superficially, it should seem surprising that many of the wives of incompetent ejaculators initiated the requests for treatment at the foundation; indeed, some of them reported frequent multiorgasmic performances in themselves, a claim that could hardly be made by the spouses of the impotent males or premature ejaculators. But, of course, most of these women were concerned that they couldn't have babies, and, besides, many of them felt that they weren't "doing the job" if they couldn't make their husbands ejaculate during intercourse.

FEMALE ORGASMIC DYSFUNCTION: A review of Masters and Johnson's earlier work on female orgasm is helpful in understanding orgasmic dysfunction (commonly called "frigidity," a term Masters and Johnson consider vague and unscientific—see discussion in chapter 2). Human sexual response is divided into four phases: *excitement,* when the woman first becomes sexually aroused and begins to lubricate; *plateau,* when she reaches a high level of stimulation and certain organs and tissues become engorged with blood; *orgasm,* when her sex tension is explosively released, characterized in the woman by involuntary vaginal and uterine contractions; and *resolution,* when muscle tension and blood congestion disappear from the pelvic area in particular and the body in general.

The woman suffering from orgasmic dysfunction does not go beyond the plateau phase. The consequences are frequently a high degree of psychic frustration combined with a slower physiological return to normal than happens in the resolution phase, and hence possible pelvic and general irritability.

Physiologically, male and female sexual response are very much alike. But where the female differs radically is in the psychosocial aspect of sexuality. Called a "sexual value system" (SVS) by the authors, it refers to those sensory experiences an individual has had under circumstances that he or she finds pleasurable, on the one hand, and, on the other, not offensive to the values he or she has learned from society (e.g., family, church, school, peer group, etc.). These experiences are stored within the person's sexual memory, to become operative in future sexual situations. As an example of a negative value, most women in this society are offended by the idea of being sexually stimulated in a nonprivate setting. So, if a couple attempted sexplay or intercourse where there was the danger of interruption and exposure, the part of the female partner's brain that sends out sexual signals to the body would probably hold those signals back: She'd fail to be stimulated (even though everything else in that particular setting was acceptable to her). There are many other negative values commonly affecting females in our society, such as taboos relating to premarital sex, touching the genitals, etc. In addition, a woman might have negative values that are purely personal—such as a dislike for a certain type of man, or of a particular man, or she may have had a trauma (such as rape), or experienced a teenage situation for which her sex education left her unprepared, etc.

An example of a positive value might be the familiar one of romantic music with the lights low, or the memory of a favored male caressing her neck, or a penchant for dark-haired men deriving from her feelings for her dark-haired father or a dark-haired first date, etc. The list is infinite, and infinitely variable, depending on who the woman is and how she grew up in society. It's important to remember that sexual values, positive and negative, are not only learned but are conditioned and imprinted in the formative years between birth and mid-adolescence.

The reason the SVS is so much more crucial in regard to female sexuality than to male is that our society has made it so difficult for women to develop positive attitudes about sex. Instead of being taught that sexual pleasure has an honorable and important place in life and thus learning to value her sexual feelings for expression under appropriate circumstances (such as, for example, marriage), the girl learns at an early age that bodily sexual pleasure is, for her, wrong; that sex is dirty and that she is expected to inhibit, distort and repress her feelings. The romantic notions that accompany her sexual yearnings are emphasized by society, but the sensory development that could turn these yearnings into concrete experience is arrested. The only desirable role assigned to sex for the woman is as it relates to reproduction, but becoming pregnant requires no sexual effectiveness at all —merely the ability to receive an ejaculating penis.

When the woman is in a sexual situation, her psychosocial sexuality interlocks with her biophysical capacity for natural sexual function. The biophysical capacity comprises all the parts of her body that are capable of responding to sexual stimulation under optimum circumstances, and all that's necessary to keep it in good shape should be a well-established metabolic balance, good nutrition, sufficient rest and regularity of sex exposure. But the circumstances are only optimum if her psychosocial sexuality says they are—and, as we have seen, there are innumerable opportunities for the signals between the psychosocial and the biophysical to be blocked, because of the many negative values and prohibitions usually stored in the former.

The psychosocial system can be so dominant that it can cause the biophysical to fail to function for a lifetime. One need only think of the old maid who has never had any sexual feeling or experience, who thinks it is evil and harmful, and who goes from womb to tomb deliberately avoiding sexual stimuli—consciously and unconsciously. She finally succeeds in denying her natural sexuality and becomes a neuter. This is not an easy task, because of the tremendous capacity for sexuality that women have, and attempting to deny it more usually leads to irritability than to sublimity. For, even when women try to "sublimate" their sexuality, they are reminded of it each month by their menstrual periods. By engorging the pelvic area with blood, the menstrual condition can stimulate elevated sexual tensions.

The nonorgasmic women entering the foundation all reflect a negative psychosocial system (SVS) that predominates over the biophysical system. When their bodies cry yes, their minds cry no, because the time, place, mood, partner or circumstances have since the early years been programmed to be considered wrong. Whether they *ever* could be reprogrammed to trigger such a woman's sensory response without professional help or redirection is doubtful.

As in impotence, there are two major categories of nonorgasmic women.

PRIMARY ORGASMIC DYSFUNCTION: Describing a woman who has never had an orgasm in her life—even in masturbation—primary orgasmic dysfunction is frequently related to a corresponding dysfunction in the woman's partner: It's not likely that a premature ejaculator or impotent male will be able to initiate his wife into orgasmic experience, much less to maintain it. And she indeed suffers a double disadvantage: fear for her partner's performance as well as for her own. The woman is also disadvantaged by the fact that traditionally she feels her fundamental function is to please her man, not herself. And she often can't trigger her biophysical component if her psychosocial component tells her she's being "used."

Among the basic causes of this distress is a background of religious orthodoxy. Of 193 women who never had orgasm, 41 came from ultrareligious backgrounds: 18 Catholic, 16 Jewish, 7 Protestant. Several cases were attributed to what the authors call "absence of dominant influence"—meaning that the woman was simply raised with no concept of herself as a sexual being. Another frequent cause was the inability of the woman to identify with her mate. He may be physically unattractive to her, or he may be a poor provider, or he may be her second-choice husband, but somehow he doesn't fit within the concept of a male that has been built into her sexual value system.

SITUATIONAL ORGASMIC DYSFUNCTION: This category comprises women who have had at least one orgasm, whether through coitus, self-manipulation, rectal penetration or oral-genital stimulation. Among the major causes are a partner perceived as "wrong" and low sexual tension. And, as with the impotent male, homosexual experience during the teens can establish a conflict that inhibits sexual responsivity in a later heterosexual situation. A critical cause is the rebound effect of the husband's sexual difficulties. In some of these cases it is almost impossible to determine which of the partners initially had the sexual dysfunction that began the chain reaction of mutually suffered difficulties.

VAGINISMUS: A classical example of a psychosomatic illness, vaginismus affects a woman's ability to respond sexually by virtually closing her vaginal opening to male entry. The woman is unable to exercise control as the muscles of the perineum and the outer third of the vagina contract spastically in response to an attempt—or an imagined attempt—at vaginal penetration. At its most severe, vaginismus totally prevents insertion of the penis. In less advanced states it simply delays or makes entry difficult. Many clinicians mistake vaginismus for a pressure-resistant hymen; once the tissue is removed, however, the problem remains.

Often this distress develops in a woman who is mated to an impotent male (the major cause of vaginismus). However, Masters and Johnson frequently could not tell which occurred first, the male or the female dysfunction. A potentially responsive woman with no apparent sexual handicap may marry a male who, it turns out, is impotent. His repeated attempts and failures at penetration raise her to a constantly high level of frustration, and this combined with her anxiety can be a cause of vaginismus. On the other hand, vaginismus may exist prior to the marriage, and when the husband is continually turned back by a virtually closed door, he loses confidence and eventually potency.

The second major cause of vaginismus is a background of religious orthodoxy. And frequently a prior sexual trauma, such as rape, will cause a woman to literally tighten up when approached in less traumatic circumstances. Fourth in order of statistical frequency is the conflict between homosexual and heterosexual identification. Vaginismus can also be caused by physical rather than psychological factors. If a woman suffers from painful intercourse, her vagina may eventually respond by constricting itself. The psychic stress under which a woman with vaginismus labors is often tipped off on the gynecologist's examining table. Many patients attempt to "escape" the doctor's approach by moving toward the head of the table, raising their legs from the stirrups or tensing their thighs to avoid the examination.

DYSPAREUNIA: In Greek, this word means "badly mated," but, in medical terminology, it has always referred to difficult or painful female intercourse. In their chapter on the subject, the authors stretch this definition to include men.

FEMALE DYSPAREUNIA: Women who wish to avoid intercourse often use pain as an excuse. Unfortunately, many clinicians, knowing this yet being ignorant of the many possible biophysical causes of pain—not to mention the combinations of psychological and physiological causes—send the women home with the admonition that it's "all in her head."

But it isn't always in her head. Real, somatic pain may be caused by an intact hymen or the irritated remnants of the hymenal ring, by scar areas in the vaginal opening, which can be the result of an episiotomy during childbirth, or by certain criminal abortion techniques, or by a gang-rape episode. The clitoris can accumulate smegma beneath its foreskin that creates a burning sensation. Infections in the vaginal barrel will result in burning, itching or aching during or after intercourse. The authors state that, typically, when women feign pain in order to avoid sex, they rarely complain of these particular symptoms; rather, they will claim severe pain deep in the pelvis with pelvic thrusting.

Masters and Johnson mention, among other causes for vaginal infection, a particular habit of many males who perform rectal intercourse with their wives. These men remove their penises from the anus just prior to ejaculation and deposit their seed in the vagina. But, the authors caution, the penis can carry infectious bacteria from the rectal area. In this same section, Masters and Johnson tell how an informed clinician can detect whether or not a patient is regularly on the receiving end of rectal intercourse:

> When the examining finger is inserted, the response of the rectal sphincter at first will be one of slight to moderate spasm, following the expected reactive pattern of most men or women undergoing routine rectal examinations. But if the examining finger is retained rectally for a few seconds, the sphincter may relax quite rapidly in a completely involuntary manner, as opposed to the routine response pattern of continuing in spastic contraction for the duration of the examination. If involuntary sphincter relaxation develops, this response pattern, while certainly not reliably diagnostic, should make the cotherapist skeptical of the patient's denial of rectal coital episodes. The involuntary sphincter relaxation develops because the retained examining finger stimulates a pleasurable response for those women enjoying regularity of rectal coital exposure as opposed to those finding rectal examinations subjectively objectionable and objectively painful.[4]

Other causes of vaginal distress include sensitivity to some of the chemicals in birth-control creams, jellies, suppositories, foams or foam tablets. Some women also react painfully to the latex in condoms or diaphragms and to repeated douching of the vagina. Masters and Johnson join most gynecologists in condemning excess douching as not only possibly dangerous, but unnecessary from the point of view of cleanliness. All that is needed to prevent postejaculatory drainage or postcoital odor is an external washing with soap and water. The douche actually may remove some of the vagina's residual acidity, which could promote the growth of bacteria and lead to infection. Moreover, some of the chemicals used in commercial douche preparations can cause irritation of the soft tissues.

Additional causes of painful intercourse include laceration of the ligaments supporting the uterus, pelvic infection, endometriosis and occasionally complications resulting from a hysterectomy operation. And, finally, if vaginal lubrication is not produced in sufficient quantities, there will be burning, itching or aching during and after intercourse.

The authors conclude the female portion of the dyspareunia chapter by pointing out that the initial approach by a physician to a complaint of painful intercourse should be a physical examination that will establish the presence or absence of infection or other physically caused distresses. Once all these possibilities are eliminated, then a search for psychosomatic causes can begin.

MALE DYSPAREUNIA: Many complaints of male pain during intercourse can be traced to the glans penis, among them an irritation caused by lack of cleanliness in the uncircumcised male. Other exotic, but unpleasant, sources of penile pain include *Peyronie's disease,* which is evidenced by an upward bowing of the penis complicated by an angulation to the left or right, and *penile chordee,* or downward bowing, which appears literally to be a broken penis. Of four men suffering from fractured phalli, two had had them slapped by angry partners, and two had had theirs sat on by eager, fumbling partners who'd lost containment in the female-superior position. In each of the cases, "something snapped," according to the memory of the victims, and ultimately the penis was bent out of shape.

A less tragic affliction, most generally experienced by adolescents and colloquially called "blueballs," reflects an unrelieved accumulation of blood in the testicles. This can result from reading erotically arousing material or indulging in unfulfilled sexplay. The symptoms vary from a dull ache to acute pain in the testicles, and the cure is ejaculation. Some males, finally, are sensitive to the birth-control chemicals used by their partners, as well as to the chemicals used in douching preparations.

SEX AND AGING: In many ways, Masters and Johnson feel that their research with the aging population is their most important work.

THE MALE: A considerable number of older men were referred to the foundation for treatment of secondary impotence, an inadequacy brought on by the assumption—shared by most of society—that sexual ability automatically declines with age. *This is not true.* What is true is that sexual physiology *changes* with age, but once the older man recognizes and adjusts to the changes, he can continue to have an effective sex life into his 80s, assuming he is in good health and that he has a partner who is interesting to him and interested in him.

The changes that occur in older men (50–70) can best be described in relation to Masters and Johnson's four phases of sexual response ("younger men," for the sake of this discussion, are aged 20–40).

In the *excitement* phase, the older man will notice a significant delay in his ability to have an erection. In the younger man, it takes seconds; after he's past 50, however, it may take minutes. Moreover, his erection may not be as full as he remembers it from earlier days. If the older man and his partner aren't panicked either by the delay or the slight penile softening, there should be no erective problems. An alert and understanding wife will help guide a semierect penis into her vagina, knowing that with a few good strokes, the male instrument will be as firm as ever.

The *plateau* phase of sexual response is where the older man shines. Once erect and inserted, he will not feel the urgent demand to ejaculate that he once did, and consequently he'll be able to exercise far better control than before. His reduced need for ejaculation must be respected, however, by himself and his partner. If, for example, he has intercourse once or twice a week at age 60, he might not need or want to ejaculate except every second or third time. If he lets this make him worry that he's not functioning properly, or if his partner feels she has failed in her role by not bringing him to ejaculation and decides to force the issue, then he may be headed for impotence.

In the *orgasmic* phase, there are a large number of changes. During the first stage of orgasm—ejaculatory inevitability— the young man feels the ejaculation coming for a period of two to four seconds and is not able to control it; in the second stage—the ejaculation—the young man's seminal fluid is expelled from the penis with enough force to travel 12 to 24 inches. As the male ages, he may not feel the stage of ejaculatory inevitability at all, or if he does, it may last a second or two; in some older men, however, it will last five to seven seconds. In the second stage of orgasm, the expulsive force of the ejaculation is usually reduced to about three to twelve inches. In addition, the quantity of seminal fluid is lessened to a little more than half its previous volume.

Perhaps one of the most frightening—because most apparent—changes is the lengthening of the period of time between erections. A young man, after ejaculating, can with proper stimulation become hard again in a few minutes. For some older men, this refractory period varies capriciously, from minutes to hours. Another change in the *resolution* phase is the older man's quick loss of erection following ejaculation. In the younger man, the penis usually takes minutes, sometimes hours, to become soft again; but the older man may lose his erection in a matter of seconds, with the penis literally dropping out of the vagina—a scary occurrence if not anticipated.

The authors stress that none of these changes need reduce the older man's subjective enjoyment of the sexual experience. Yet many men, sensing a difference in physiological function, begin to fear that they are losing their ability. These men are victims of a cultural fallacy which equates inconsistency of performance with loss of masculinity.

THE FEMALE: Women in our society also tend to give up on their sexuality at an age when it is hardly necessary to do so. As with the male, physiological changes occur in the 50–70-year female age group, but these changes need not prevent full sexual response if the woman remains healthy, performs regularly and retains a high place for sexuality in her sexual value system (not an easy task in a society that thinks "decent" older people—especially women—should do little more than stay home in bed—alone).

In the *excitement* phase of the female sexual-response cycle, the younger woman (20–40 years) will lubricate (the precise equivalent of male erection) in 15 to 30 seconds. But as she ages, it may take her anywhere from one to five minutes of sexplay before she produces enough lubrication to insure a comfortable intromission. The reduced pace of lubrication is caused by the fact that *all* physiological responses are slowed down by age and also, in Masters and Johnson's words, by a "natural involution of ovarian function." [5] This means the woman may be lacking a sufficient supply of hormones in her system, the result of which will be a constriction in size of the vaginal barrel and a thinning and deterioration of the vaginal walls. In addition, the flexibility of the vagina is markedly reduced with age. Normally, the vagina is a potential rather than an actual space; its walls collapse together when not in use, but expand as necessary for penile intromission or even to accommodate a baby's head. These changes in the vaginal walls can be partially compensated for by sex-hormone-replacement techniques, which are increasingly recognized today by qualified clinicians as supporting not only the older woman's sexual life but her total health and well-being.

During the *plateau* phase of sexual response, the uterus of the older woman is not elevated as high as previously (this is one more factor that reduces the potential expansion of the vagina). In addition, there is a change in coloration of the minor labia and a loss of elevation of the major labia. Although there may be a small reduction in clitoral size during the postmenopausal years (60–70), there does not appear to be any loss in sensitivity.

The *orgasm* is considerably shorter for the older woman. Her vaginal contractions drop from a pattern of eight to twelve in the younger group to four or five for older women. The same is true for the contractions of the uterus, which drop from an average of three to five to one or two. Many women in need of sex-hormone replacement will feel a spastic tightening rather than recurrent contractions of the uterus, and this can be very painful.

In the *resolution* phase, finally, the pelvic structure of the aging woman will return to an unstimulated state following orgasm more rapidly than in her younger days.

THE THERAPISTS

So far, the patients who are treated at the Reproductive Biology Research Foundation and their sexual dysfunctions have been discussed; let's take a look now at the therapy concepts and the therapists who do the treatment.

The laboratory for investigation of human sexual response was established in 1954. The premise behind the study of sexual intercourse in the laboratory was that it was necessary to learn all that was possible about the physiology and anatomy of normal sexual functioning before tackling the less measurable and more complex psychological areas involved in human sexual dysfunction. Medical science has always followed this principle with regard to the other bodily systems and their functions. The results of the laboratory's first 11-year study were published in *Human Sexual Response* (Little, Brown, 1966). The second study began in 1959, and the results of this 11-year clinical program are contained in *Human Sexual Inadequacy* (Little, Brown, 1970). Future reports will deal with homosexual response and concepts concerning the prevention of sexual dysfunction.

One of the basic ideas involved in all the research and treatment at the foundation is that no man can completely understand female sexual response or dysfunction, nor can any woman totally understand that of the male. For this and other reasons, all treatment is given by dual-sex therapy teams: a man and a woman. It helps the patient of either sex—for example, the woman—who may be having difficulty communicating with her spouse, to know that a sympathetic female therapist is there to interpret for her. The converse is also true, of course. Moreover, the emotional and sexual language barriers that exist between many husbands and wives are more easily broken down with the help of an understanding and authoritative man and woman.

In single-counselor therapy, where the therapist is usually a male, if criticism is made of the wife, justified as it may be, she may feel she's the victim of a gang-up by the two men and communication will break down. Also, Masters and Johnson feel that a woman talking to a male therapist will first tell him "what she wants him to know; second, what she thinks he wants to know or can understand; and not until a third, ultimately persuasive attempt has been made can she consistently be relied upon to present material as it is or as it really appears to her."[6] If a female cotherapist is in the room, the dissembling will end quicker, on the recognition by the patient that "it takes one to know one." Conversely, the fragile ego of the male will be less abused if he is not forced to "impress" a female therapist, but can rather tell it like it is to another man. A second closely related advantage of the dual-sex team is that patients of neither sex feel they have to indulge in social rituals akin to flirting in order to gain the confidence of an opposite-sex counselor.

If the patient is tempted to do any inaccurate reporting to either member of the dual-sex team, the temptation will be curbed by the knowledge that he'll be seeing the other member—and probably both together—before the week is over, at which time he'll be exposed.

A final advantage of the dual-sex team is that the patient is not encouraged to indulge in "transference," a technique used in other psychotherapies in which the client is encouraged to strongly identify with the counselor as a means of building confidence in the treatment. Transference is discouraged at the foundation, partly because it is time-consuming, but mostly because Masters and Johnson wish the husband and wife to identify with *each other* rather than with the therapists. In fact, when a patient is detected paying more attention to the team members than to his or her spouse, a conscious effort is made by the team to change the direction of the discussion.

Apart from requiring that the two team members be of different sexes, the foundation prefers, also, that they come from separate professional disciplines. Generally, one is from the biological (medical) sciences, and the other, the behavioral. Reflecting this, Dr. Masters is a specialist in gynecology; Mrs. Johnson, an experienced psychologist. On the foundation's second team, Richard Spitz is a pediatrician; Sally Schumacher, a clinical psychologist. A medical person is desirable on each team because of the necessity to do a thorough evaluation of the patient's physical health before beginning psychological therapy. As mentioned in the "Dyspareunia" section, a number of complaints thought to be in the mind are actually in the body.

Perhaps the most important requirement to be a member of a dual-sex therapy team is a thorough and comfortable knowledge of the therapist's own sexuality. In order to exude confidence and maintain objectivity while dealing in areas that are delicate and controversial, the team members must have an established sense of security and stability in their own personal lives. Obviously, this type of occupation is not recommended for the person who is struggling to work out his own sexual hang-ups.

To summarize: The therapy team's function is to act as a catalyst (1) to an understanding by the husband and wife of their sexual distress and its causes, (2) to restoring sex to its natural pattern, and (3) to helping establish communication in an area that is inevitably fraught with fear, embarrassment, misunderstanding, anger and defensive armor.

THE TREATMENT

The rapid therapy administered at the Reproductive Biology Research Foundation takes a total of two weeks and consists of a combination of interviewing and physical-therapy sessions that are practiced by the distressed couple in the privacy of their hotel or rented apartment. The ultimate purpose of the therapy is to restore sex to its natural context, so that it functions, as it should, like breathing—spontaneously and without conscious effort. Sex, of course, is unique among physiological functions in that it can be delayed and denied indefinitely. This quality can be a great advantage in a busy, complex society, because it allows us to defer our sexual impulses when they are untimely or inappropriate. But somewhere along the road to building our society, we confused the healthy, civilized control of sexuality with almost total repression of it. Those who suffer most acutely from this confusion are the patients at the foundation. They have to be helped—by word and deed—to breach the formidable barriers their life experiences have erected against their natural desires.

The first step in this direction consists of history taking with the emphasis on relating the patients' sexual past to their basic personality structure and to the context of the rest of their lives—in other words, their sexual value system. The couple is informed up front that the interviews will be taped and that they will not be asked to perform as subjects for laboratory experiments. The format of the first day's history is male therapist with male patient, female with female.

On the second day, the therapist-and-patient teams are switched, and the interviews are structured on material obtained the preceding day.

The third day includes medical examinations and a round-table discussion among the husband, wife and therapists. The foursome format emphasizes that it is the marital relationship and not its members that is being treated. During the round-table, one of the most important concepts in sexual dysfunction—*the spectator role*—is explained in detail. Using the example of erective inadequacy, the therapists explain how the impotent male suffers from being overaware of his (and his partner's) responses. Instead of becoming immersed in the natural sensory feelings that accompany the growth of an erection, he tries self-consciously, by the numbers, to will the raising of his penis with his mind, literally setting his intelligence apart from his senses, so that it is a "spectator" observing an action unrelated to it. The bedroom spectator can no more influence the stiffening of his penis than a football grandstander can cheer a pigskin across the line. The erection must occur naturally, like breathing, or it will not occur at all.

The wife in this situation often becomes a spectator, too. Leaving her own sensory responses, she places her mind outside the arena and observes her progress and her partner's progress—or lack of it. Frequently she herself becomes so absorbed in the spectator role that she's unable to respond when the opportunity is provided.

By the end of the third day, the patients have given clues to the therapists about their individual sexual value systems—what turns them on and what turns them off—and they have heard authoritatively suggested forms of sexual interaction that might have been unfamiliar—or even forbidden—to them. From then on, the aim of the therapy will be to help the patients lose the negative values of the SVS, retain the positive ones and add new experiences and values that are appropriate to their ongoing relationship.

Implicit in the Masters and Johnson therapy is the evidence that people with sexual dysfunctions have been negatively conditioned to sex during their formative years. The therapists attempt to decondition the inhibiting values and recondition new, positive values (see chapter 7 for a description of the relatively new science of behavior therapy). Negative-type values, usually learned early in life when comparatively few experiences are required to make an enduring mark, were explained individually in earlier sections of this chapter. Just to recapitulate with a single example, the little girl's hand is slapped when she touches her genitals; she may become conditioned to a "no-no" reaction when her genitals are touched at any time in later life—even by herself or her husband, because the person who slapped her hand did not attempt to distinguish for the child when it is appropriate or inappropriate to touch.

Masters and Johnson attempt not only to decondition these negative values, but they try to recondition new ones that will be remembered with positive connotations when the patients resume their normal lives. The therapists assume that the only *psychological* constant in human sexual response is the memory of pleasurable sensate reactions. It is these memories that, when combined with the input of a new experience, serve to facilitate the signals from the brain to the genitals that result in uninhibited sexual response.

The therapists attempt to initiate this relearning process by starting with the senses. Since they are central to sexual response, an effort is made to bring the patient back into contact with them (bearing in mind, as just explained, that he has become a "spectator" to his sensory reactions because he has lost the ability to *feel* them). The core of "sensate focus," as Masters and Johnson term it, is the sense of touch, because most individuals have been conditioned to associate touch with the communication of such positive emotions as comfort, solace, reassurance, devotion, love and physical need. By refocusing the patient's awareness of his sense of touch, the therapists begin to decondition his physical restraint. The other senses—smell, sight, hearing—are not approached directly, but they come into play and serve as a reinforcement of the touching experience.

The exercises to accomplish this are not introduced until the third day. The couple is instructed to retire to their private quarters at a time when they feel a minimum of stress and tension, when they're rested and don't fear interruption. They take all their clothes off. One of the partners is arbitrarily designated the "giver of pleasure," the other is delegated to "get pleasure." Assuming the giver is the male, he uses his fingers and hands to touch, massage, fondle his partner's body—but not her genitals or her breasts. The "getting" partner simply tries to relax and become enveloped in sensory pleasure. If the giver has some notion of what his partner likes, he pays special attention to it; if he doesn't, a gentle trial-and-error method is used. The only taboos, besides avoidance of the genitalia, are that both partners eschew discomfort, distraction, irritation and any sense of compulsion to verbally communicate their pleasure. This may be the first opportunity, the authors explain, for the couple to have a sensory experience without pushing for orgasm, "without need to explain their sensate preferences, without the demand for personal reassurance, or without a sense of need to rush to 'return the favor.' " [7]

After a while, the partners change assignments and soon begin to lose the initial sense of artificiality. It is at this point that the therapist's role as catalyst begins to diminish and the patients begin to be on their own.

A fascinating discovery serendipitously developed out of the touch therapy. In response to complaints by patients that dry and rough hands distracted from the pleasures of touching and feeling, Masters and Johnson commissioned the creation of a special lotion, which at the same time was used to test fragrance preferences among the patients and to enhance the touching by reducing skin friction. The fragrance tests were abandoned as inconclusive for the present study, but the therapists were unwittingly provided with a useful tool as a result of their lotion experiments. One of the hang-ups experienced by many sexually inhibited individuals is a feeling of discomfort with the sexual fluids—the woman's vaginal lubrication, the man's seminal fluid. Touching each other with the lotions, many of the patients gradually became accustomed to the feel of liquid during a sexual encounter and consequently lost this inhibition.

The exercises designed to enhance "sensate focus" are continued through the fourth day of therapy, after which permission is given for the couple to include the genitals and female breasts in their touch sessions. A lesson in sexual anatomy, with specific reference to the husband understanding the female genitalia, is given, and permission is also given for the partners to verbally express enjoyment during their training periods. However, the couple should never be made to feel that this is a necessary part of the "pleasuring" process, because the inhibited type of individual who needs this kind of therapy is frequently distracted by verbalization during sexual activity.

With the termination of the fourth day of therapy—all four days approximately the same for any kind of sexual distress—attention is thereafter directed to the individual's or couple's specific dysfunction.

(A footnote should be added here about "replacement partners and partner surrogates." Obviously, there are individuals suffering from sexual distress who are not married. But since the foundation's techniques are based on interaction between partners, how can they treat an unmarried client? There are two answers. Thirteen men and three women brought partners of their choice to whom they were not married. These were called *replacement partners*. And 41 men were provided with female partners [*not* prostitutes] who volunteered their help to the foundation. These women were called *partner surrogates*. See chapter 2 for a discussion of this by Dr. Masters and Mrs. Johnson.)

IMPOTENCE: To state the obvious, a marriage in which the husband is impotent—primary or secondary—is a relationship in which the partners are sexual strangers. Very often, the wife has herself developed symptoms of a sexual distress as a result of trying to cope with this frustrating estrangement. The focus of therapy is to acquaint or reacquaint these sexually alienated people with each other. Many times, the sexual alienation has been the cause of additional estrangements within the marriage.

First, the couple must be helped to understand that sexual response encompasses a series of sensate feedbacks, one partner to the other. With dysfunctional couples, one or more of these feedbacks has become blocked. Had they been functioning naturally, they would have followed either or both of two basic patterns: (1) He approaches her, emitting a nonverbal signal that he is interested. Her awareness of this stimulates her, and she responds physically with some or all of the following reactions: Her muscles become taut, she breathes rapidly, her face becomes flushed, her vagina begins to lubricate. His response to these messages of invitation is further arousal, including the development of an erection. The mutual feedback continues until they have successfully performed intercourse. (2) In the other pattern, she may approach him first, and the same system of mutual feedback begins.

These patterns can malfunction in a number of ways. If he approaches her, and she does not return the arousal signal —in other words, shows no pleasure in his approach, perhaps because they had quarreled or she is fatigued or preoccupied —then his feedback mechanism becomes blocked. The automatic arousal of sensory stimulation that would have occurred if he'd received a welcoming signal does not occur, resulting in no erection or at best a partial erection. If he becomes self-conscious about this, the nonverbal sensory-signal system breaks down further. He has brought his intellect into the act—as a spectator—and he will probably try to will an erection. Failure is almost assured, and this will be followed by panic, thus assuring further failure. By the same principle, if she approaches first, and he regards her approach with his intellect rather than with his senses, he will be inviting the failure cycle.

In impotence therapy the partners are taught that there is "nothing to fear but fear itself," the first step in removing the causes of fear. The same is done for husband *and* wife, because by demonstrating concern for his performance, she merely increases his fears about his manhood. Presumably, once fear is taken out of the arena, the partners become actors rather than spectators. Accordingly, they are then taught not only to give pleasure, but to remove any blocks that prevent the getting of pleasure, so that both can lose themselves in natural sensory enjoyment. Masters and Johnson call this "giving-to-get."

The specific techniques used to achieve these goals are relatively simple. Once the sensate-focus exercises have been absorbed by the partners, they are instructed to indulge in genital and female-breast play, but without trying for lubrication or erection. If the male does begin to have an erection —and he generally does, simply because no demand is being made of him—he is encouraged to let it become soft, make it hard again, let it become soft, etc. This helps teach him that there are more erections where the last one came from and that a loss of firmness is not necessarily a permanent loss. It also gives the wife confidence in her stimulative skill and, what's more, it stimulates her.

During these sessions, as the couple begins to see tangible success and gains faith in the therapists, they, in turn, direct their attention to some of the nonsexual aspects of the distressed marriage. Counselors capable of miraculously erecting a firm penis, where there was only flab before, will be trusted to help rebuild other parts of the relationship. At the same time, the couple is encouraged to talk about their mistakes during the practice sessions—laughingly, if possible. This is to emphasize the fact that there are no grades given for "good" performance, nor failing marks for "poor" ones, an attitude that helps the couple relax and consequently perform better. Many therapists fail because, at some point, they tell the client, "Tonight's the night," which immediately rearouses all the old fears and destroys whatever effectiveness the therapy may have had up to then. Not only does the foundation never demand performance, but it actually forbids intercourse during the initial days of therapy, regardless of the number and quality of erections the male may achieve.

The trick in Masters and Johnson's impotence therapy is to let the wife initiate the first attempt at intercourse. On or about the tenth day, she is told to place herself in the female-superior position, with her husband on his back. (Figure 1) At the appropriate time, and while manipulating his penis, *she* inserts it and holds it firmly in her vagina, moving slowly, when she moves, but never thrusting vigorously. (Many men with firm erections begin to lose them when they are forced to find the elusive entrance themselves: The loss of continuity in sensate pleasure gives them a chance to start thinking and

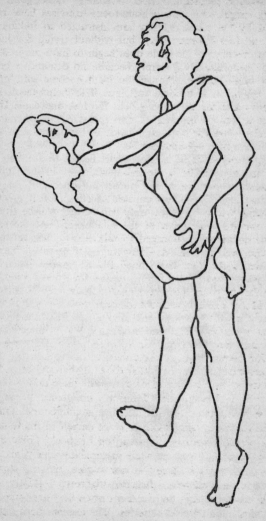

Figure 1

fearing again, regressing them to the spectator role, once more to witness another *no*-act bedroom farce.)

The exercise just described is repeated several times, with the wife continuing to move slowly. This helps allay his fear, once in the vagina, that he may lose his erection. If his penis does get soft, she gets off and manipulates it until it is hard again; if it stays soft, the session is over. Once this exercise is successfully accomplished, the wife is instructed to be still while the husband thrusts. In the final days, the couple is encouraged to engage in simultaneous "pelvic pleasuring," with no other purpose than to concentrate on the sensory pleasure involved, she in containment, he in being contained. Ejaculation and orgasm are not to be aimed at, though they will occur—in due time, and in their natural context, indicating that the symptoms have been reversed.

When practiced for the full 14 days, these techniques worked in 19 of 32 primary-impotence cases (for a success ratio of 59.4%) and 157 of 213 secondary-impotence cases (for a ratio of 73.8%). Masters and Johnson, who give their statistics in terms of failure rather than success, judge any case a failure if the couple does not continue to function effectively for at least five years after leaving the foundation.

PREMATURE EJACULATION: The two basic aims of premature-ejaculation therapy are to re-establish mutual respect and understanding between marital partners for each other's sexual-response patterns and to teach the male, by a process of physical reconditioning, how to exercise control over his ejaculation.

The physical-reconditioning process begins shortly after the round-table discussions, at which time the wife is instructed to manipulate her husband's penis in any manner found acceptable to both partners. This is done in the following position: She sits on the bed, her legs spread and her back against the headboard, while he lies on his back, his head toward the other end of the bed and his legs draped over her thighs, so that she has free access to his genitals. (Figure 2) When he achieves a full erection, she locates the ridge of his penis and places her thumb on the part closest to his body; then her first and second fingers are placed on the other side of the penile ridge. Now she squeezes with considerable pressure for three or four seconds. This will cause

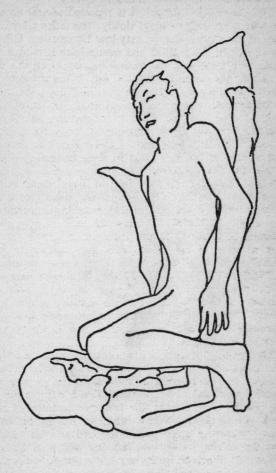

Figure 2

him to lose 10 to 30 percent of his erection (and if he were close to the stage of ejaculatory inevitability, he'd lose the urge to come as well). Fifteen to 30 seconds of inactivity are allowed, and then she starts manipulating again, and again squeezes when he feels the orgasmic urge. Properly done—about four or five times—the couple can manage 15 to 20 minutes of sexplay before he ejaculates. This exercise, practiced for two or three days, not only helps him achieve an increasing measure of control but teaches her to judge his various levels of excitement (an important step in establishing communication).

In the next step, she assumes the female-superior position and, after inserting his penis, remains motionless. This acquaints him with the feeling of the vaginal environment (he may never have been there for more than a few seconds at a time before) and gives him confidence that it's not a fuse designed to detonate a penile explosion. Eventually, he'll feel he *is* about to explode—just prior to the phase of ejaculatory inevitability—and, communicating this to his wife, she elevates herself and applies the squeeze technique.

It follows as the day the night that the wife of a prematurely orgasmic man will be afflicted with the opposite inadequacy: no coital orgasms at all. Therefore, after he has been taught the rudiments of control, attention is given to her, with emphasis on learning to feel and think sexually while she is practicing these pleasurable exercises.

Once the couple has learned to manage 15 to 20 minutes of motionless and slow-motion intercourse in the female-superior position, they are taught to begin using the side-by-side position. (Figure 3) This position allows him to exercise maximum control, and it imposes on both partners a minimum of cramping, pinning and body pressure—as opposed, for example, to the male-superior position, which provides the least control and the least freedom of any position.

At the conclusion of the 14-day regimen, he will have learned what control is all about, but he will still not be totally secure with it. The couple is told that once home, they should maintain regularity of sex exposure, and should practice the squeeze technique at least once a week. By combining unprogramed intercourse with the newly learned

Figure 3

exercise, a gradual transition from one to the other will occur—perhaps within six months.

A couple of cautions are provided by Masters and Johnson:

¶The squeeze technique does not work when applied by a male to himself.

¶Some couples, so overjoyed by their new-found sexual skill, tend to treat it as a child treats a new toy: without moderation. Eventually the male may become fatigued and find his penis unwilling to play. He then becomes flooded with new fears (his old insecurity hardly dissipated) and he risks becoming a secondary-impotence case.

Of 186 men treated for premature ejaculation at the foundation, 182 cases were successful—for a ratio of 97.8%. This is the best record the foundation has achieved, and it indicates why Masters and Johnson are confident that the symptoms of this inadequacy are almost invariably reversible —*if* the female cooperates and the male wants them reversed.

EJACULATORY INCOMPETENCE: Contrary to much of the lore about this distress, as well as about premature ejaculation, it is not a form of impotence—for the obvious reason that in neither case does the victim have difficulty in establishing an erection. In fact, these two dysfunctions are considered by Masters and Johnson to be direct counterparts of each other—in one, the man comes involuntarily; in the other, he cannot voluntarily come—and the treatment for ejaculatory incompetence follows the basic pattern of that for premature ejaculation. Except that in the former, the female partner is instructed *not* to help her husband avoid ejaculation; rather, she uses vigorous manipulative techniques to encourage his orgasm. She asks him what feels best, she employs lotions, she uses her hands to play actively with his penis. Though it may take a considerable amount of time, when he does ejaculate, he has begun to overcome the psychological barrier concerning his wife. Masters and Johnson report, "When she has brought him pleasure, he identifies with her (not infrequently for the first time in the marriage) as a pleasure symbol rather than as a threat or as an objectionable, perhaps contaminated, sexual image." [8]

Not only does she bring him pleasure by helping him clear his psychologically blocked penile passage, but she inevitably demonstrates her own pleasure in doing so. This is an important step in restructuring what has probably been a fractured marriage (and, as in all the treatments, the therapists move in quickly to help the other parts of the faltering relationship, once having established a certain degree of confidence in the couple).

The next step within the privacy of the bedroom is for the wife, in the female-superior position, to rapidly insert the male's penis into her vagina when he says he is about to ejaculate. Having done this, she moves briskly and will probably catch at least a portion of the man's seminal fluid in her vagina. This is another major block conquered. With three or four episodes like this, they are ready to begin having intercourse with progressively less precoital play and are well on their way to recovery.

Of 17 men treated at the foundation, 14 were able to overcome the problem, for a success ratio of 82.4%.

FEMALE ORGASMIC DYSFUNCTION: The key to helping a woman resolve her inability to have an orgasm is an understanding of her sexual value system, bearing in mind that the necessity to have "permission" to be sexual is relevant to the woman rather than to the man in this society. Many women need to develop a "bridge" from early rejection to acceptance of their sexual identity. In the early interviewing, the therapists carefully glean what the woman's sexual attitudes are, what she likes about having sex with her husband and what she doesn't like. She may be expecting more than he can offer, or what he offers may be repulsive to her; either way, her sensory responses are blocked. The woman and her husband also have discussions with the therapists after each sensate-focus exercise, so that they can determine what turned her on and what turned her off. Her reactions to these touch-and-feel sessions sometimes give a clue to what kind of sexual imprinting she has had. As defined by John Money, a Johns Hopkins psychologist, and reported by Masters and Johnson, imprinting "is a process whereby a perceptual signal is matched to an innate releasing mechanism which elicits a behavioral pattern. Established at critical periods in development, imprints thereafter are considered more or less permanent."[9] As applied to the nonorgasmic woman, she may be imprinted with a desire for close body contact or a revulsion from it. Having some notion about this helps the therapists understand what her emotional biases are regarding touch.

Before getting into the private session of bedroom therapy, the couple is asked to understand that the female partner will have to learn to respond to sexual stimuli as correlated between her shared experiences with her partner and her own personal concept of time, place, circumstances, expectations, etc. Thus, a bridge will have to be built connecting her sexual *feelings* and *attitudes,* through verbal and physical communication between her and her partner. The changes in her attitude that will generally be necessary involve securing "permission" for her to find pleasure in and to honor her expression of sexuality. These changes in attitude must, of course, be consistent with her social and moral codes if they are to be internalized and retained following therapy.

The specific treatment for the nonorgasmic woman, following the sensate-focus sessions which presumably have established an appreciation of generalized sensate pleasure, begins with male manipulation of her genital area. The man sits on the bed with his back against the headboard; she sits between his legs, her back against his chest, and throws her legs over his (thereby spreading hers). (Figure 4) She places her hand on his and guides it gently to show him what she likes and dislikes.

In his manipulation of her sexual parts, the male is cautioned against directly stimulating the head of the clitoris (clitoral glans), as this is often extremely sensitive and can be painful as the woman becomes excited. She also can be overwhelmed by the rapid sensation caused by clitoral stimulation. Females, when masturbating, in fact, rarely touch the clitoral glans directly. Stimulation should be conducted in *the area of* the clitoris as well as on the inner thighs and the genital lips. Lubrication should be brought from the mouth of the vagina to the clitoral area to reduce the possibility of irritation. Finger manipulation of the vaginal opening is also found by many women to be pleasurable.

An additional "tease" technique that is recommended involves the male's lightly moving his fingers from her breasts to her stomach to her thighs to her outer lips and back again, without remaining very long in the genital area. This

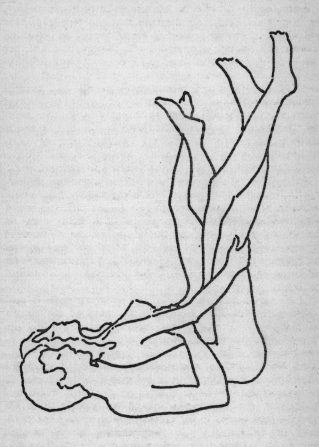

Figure 4

can be combined with stroking techniques that were learned during the sensate-focus sessions.

As in all therapy, both partners are discouraged from striving for orgasm; they're advised just to drift in sensory pleasure. Moreover, exercises are introduced in layers, each representing a different component of the woman's sexuality. After the initial or core exercise is practiced successfully, it is repeated together with the next layer. And the next, and so on.

An important step is introduced when the woman is told to mount her husband in the female-superior position and, after inserting his penis in her vagina, to remain still in order to enjoy the feeling of penile containment. Following this, she may institute a period of slow, controlled pelvic thrusting, with the man remaining relatively inert and merely providing the necessary tool for her use. Her languorous pelvic thrusting may be accelerated if and when she *feels* an involuntary urge to do so. After several sessions of this, she may begin to experience vaginal sensation, at which point she is instructed to signal her partner to begin a complementary and unhurried pelvic movement.

When the couple can enjoyably perform this exercise, without feeling any compulsion to press for orgasm, they are instructed to take breaks two or three times during a total episode. While resting, they are encouraged to lie quietly and caressingly in each other's arms. They then resume intercourse. If they can manage this game without ejaculation or vigorous pelvic thrusting, they have achieved a major step. The authors say, "Women have little opportunity to feel and think sexually while pursuing or receiving a pattern of forceful pelvic thrusting before their own encompassing levels of excitation are established." [10] In actuality, if the woman initiates thrusting, it may be because she is trying to *will* an orgasm; if he initiates it, she may lose her enjoyment of quiet sensate pleasure by trying to keep up with him.

Having successfully completed this progression of steps, the couple then enters the final phase, which is intercourse in the side-by-side position. Because of the better ejaculatory control provided by this position, and because it allows the woman to regulate her own pelvic thrusting, she usually achieves orgasm before the rapid-treatment period is ended.

Of 193 women with primary orgasmic dysfunction, 161 were treated successfully, for a ratio of 83.4%; of 149 situational cases, 105 were successful, for a rate of 77.2%. The over-all success rate was 80.7%.

VAGINISMUS: First, the involuntary constriction of the outer third of the vagina is explained in detail to the couple, on paper and on the examining table. The difficulty of inserting a finger into the spastic opening is demonstrated by the physician/therapist to the husband and to the often surprised wife. Then the husband himself is encouraged to try. Once both partners fully realize the nature of the problem, the physician uses dilating instruments to relieve it—in about three to five days. Following physical relief, the couple is involved in discussions of the causes. Masters and Johnson feel that the combination of physical therapy and an authoritative dissemination of sex information is usually sufficient to send the couple home functioning effectively.

Of 29 vaginismic women, all were relieved of their spasms; 20 were introduced to orgasm for the first time, six regained their previous orgasmic ability, and three remained non-orgasmic.

THE AGING POPULATION: Apart from the need for hormone replacement, the complaints brought by aging couples are essentially the same as discussed throughout *Human Sexual Inadequacy.* The success rate among men over 50 was zero out of one for primary impotence (0%); 18 of 28, secondary impotence (64.3%); and 19 of 20, premature ejaculation (94.7%). In the aging female group, 50 to 70 years, there were 9 successes out of 15, primary orgasmic dysfunction (60%); 7 of 12, situational orgasmic dysfunction (58.4%). There were a number of younger wives of older men, aged 28 to 49, who were included in this group. Their success rate was 6 of 8, primary orgasmic dysfunction (75%); 4 of 6, situational orgasmic dysfunction (66.7%).

FAILURES

Not only do Masters and Johnson discuss their therapy results in terms of failure rather than success, but they also devote a chapter specifically to the subject of failure. The purpose is to discuss their mistakes and shed light on the pitfalls of sexual-inadequacy therapy for other practitioners.

One of the expected causes of therapeutic failure is an irretrievably fractured marriage. Not only does this situation reflect a breakdown in therapy—since no counselor can restore a relationship in which the partners have committed themselves to hatred, vengeance and eventual dissolution—but an error in screening. The partners in such a marriage should not be admitted for rapid treatment in the first place.

Another cause of failure is extreme patient anxiety. In some cases, the anxiety is caused by simple apprehension about what the treatment entails and what the married couple has left behind, but just as often it may relate to a concern about deep, dark secrets in one of the partners' backgrounds, disclosure of which appears disastrous to that individual. One patient had had an incestuous relationship with her father, and there was a great deal of fear, on her part as well as on the therapists', that revelation of that information might be more destructive to the marriage than the wife's lack of sexual responsivity. The therapists decided to cooperate in withholding the information, reflecting, in their opinion, a mistake.

Still another therapeutic pitfall involves individuals who arrive at the foundation with a great deal of time clocked in at other psychotherapists' offices and, as a possible consequence, an equally great deal of cynicism and hostility toward all therapists. Frequently, these attitudes are never overcome.

Interference by other therapists can create a disastrous situation while the couple is at the foundation. One woman constantly consulted with her referring counselor by phone while she was being treated—without letting her husband or the foundation team know about it. This diffusion of authority led to predictably unsalutary results.

The final category of failure involved not the foundation's mistakes, nor those of its personnel, but the blunders of other psychotherapists. These are individuals who, in the opinion of Masters and Johnson, unscrupulously seduce their patients. This practice results in failures, the authors feel, because even if the patient is brought to an effective level of response by the therapist, he or she rarely will be able to achieve or maintain that level back at the ranch—for the simple reason that the identification of these individuals is directed toward their therapists rather than to their spouses. There is bound to be considerable controversy over this revelation, because Masters and Johnson identify a large segment of the counseling profession, from psychiatrists to marriage counselors to clergymen of every faith, as participating in this practice. The authors consider it shabbily and exploitively unprofessional.

FOOTNOTES: From *Human Sexual Inadequacy,* by William H. Masters and Virginia E. Johnson (Boston, 1970).

[1] pages 139–140
[2] page 179
[3] pages 187–188
[4] pages 271–272
[5] page 336
[6] page 6
[7] page 73
[8] page 129
[9] page 295
[10] pages 308–309

2

MASTERS AND JOHNSON DISCUSS HUMAN SEXUAL INADEQUACY

On April 20, 21 and 22, 1970, at Boston's Ritz-Carlton hotel, Masters and Johnson conducted a press conference the nature of which is rare, if not unprecedented, in book-publishing annals. Anticipating an influx of science writers that might approach the size of a presidential press confab, and fearing that theirs might be just as stilted and un-informative, the authors divided the group into six parts and rapped with each subgroup for two hours apiece. The discussions were breezy and informal, and judging from the tremendously widespread and intelligent press coverage of the book (including a cover story in Time*), the results were magnificent. The tapes of these meetings were tran-scribed and I edited them into about 20,000 words of compact comment about* Human Sexual Inadequacy *by its authors. Because of the difficulty of their writing, as op-posed to the clarity of their speech, Masters and Johnson's elucidation of their own work should not only provide informative reading, but should also prove useful to scholars wishing to interpret fine points of the text.*

THERAPY PROCEDURE

Q: Would you discuss briefly the therapy procedure?
J: Our history taking occupies approximately seven hours of the 25 to 50 collective hours that will be spent in directive therapy during the two-week period. The seven hours, in which we try to develop a working knowledge of each member of the marriage *and* their relationship, are divided in this fashion: The first day's history is taken by a therapist of the same sex, and it's the longest interview—it runs about two hours. I take a little longer under some circumstances; Dr. Masters talks a little longer on others; but, nevertheless, the average time will always be about two hours for the history by the same sex. It is longer than the others because the initial interview establishes a chronological order which will be followed in subsequent discussions. On the second day we switch sexes. The female therapist takes a supplemental history from the male patient, coloring, extending and/or altering for accuracy material obtained the first day, and vice versa. In the meantime, both therapists would have exchanged basic details coming out of the first session. We tape everything. Let me make clear—this is our form of recordkeeping. First of all, we found taping to be the most reliable way to protect the material, because the minute you add a secretary, you risk losing privacy and anonymity. We have an exquisite security system to protect the tapes. Second, since nuance may be the crucial thing, the tape also is available so that a cotherapist, who is not present during a particular occasion, can hear the patient verbatim.
Q: Is that invariable—same-sex interviews the first day, opposite-sex the second?
J: Correct. This and the approximate time spent are constant for ourselves as well as our other therapy teams. What does this do? First of all, it usually makes recall a little easier by putting the patient at his (or her) ease, making him feel comfortable, letting him feel he's talking to a "friend in court" rather than having the potential burden of first working through the man/woman social ritual; also, the same sex pursuing material that is familiar to that sex may establish an accurate base line of information faster.

Q: How's the balance of the therapy time spent?

M: That depends. Remember, the married couple is with us for two solid weeks. In many modes of psychotherapy the meetings may take place once or twice a week. But in that 50 minutes to an hour of therapy, one has to say hello, one has to reaffirm the relationship and then pick up possible loose ends from the previous session. All of that essentially is eliminated in our procedure. However, to answer your question: Following the history taking of the first two days, the patients start "looking in a mirror" with the round-table discussion of the third day. From then on, we bring about two things. One, by our suggestion, the couple alters specific patterns of mutual behavior, which in turn begin to reverse the sexual dysfunction, which is really what they are there for; but, just as important, we use this time to reconstitute the marital relationship. This, of course, is vital to their *maintaining* effective sexual function after it is attained. And we do it first by establishing confidence in the therapists (which could be called transference) and second by acting as catalysts to satisfactory verbal and physical communication between the husband and wife. You see, as the patients see the symptoms of the sexual dysfunction begin to disappear, they are more and more interested in what we have to suggest in terms of their total relationship. This is the direction in which we move, and we move at each couple's pace and facility for accepting new material.

Q: Didn't you used to conduct therapy during a three-week period?

M: Yes, but we now think two weeks is quite sufficient. Three weeks tends to develop an unrealistic focus on the sexual part of the marriage.

J: You must remain as close as possible to the context of the people's own lives, to their own life style. In other words, there's a limit even on vacations as to how much they can take themselves out of their normal, familiar way of living. People who vacation happily for one week and enjoy two weeks may find it absolutely unbearable for three.

Q: Do you consider it preferable for people seeking this kind of counseling to leave their home towns and go to a different place?

M: If they can arrange any sort of semi-isolation during the time they're being treated, their response to the therapy process will be more rapid and easier to maintain. Trying to take the treatment and meet all the other commitments—social, business—of a normal life disturbs the continuity of the treatment. You must remember that this involves daily therapy sessions on a seven-days-a-week basis.

J: What Bill is suggesting is that a great deal of sexual dysfunction often has been compounded by the fact that sexual expression has been put aside for other demands, or given lesser priority, and so, if the couple remain in their own environment, they tend to continue any established pattern which places priorities on other things—you know, shopping, cleaning, crying babies, telephones, the relatives, neighbors, and so on, all to the detriment of the therapy.

Q: Do the people maintain any telephone contact with their home environments?

J: Yes. It's one thing to remain in contact and it's another to be available for every petition for fund raising, for the next-door neighbor, for the kid down the street, for the mother-in-law, etc.

M: It may seem that two weeks in relative isolation is a great deal, but if you stop and think about it, it's not much more in terms of isolation than what might be required for medical surgery.

PARTNER SURROGATES

Q: One of the things that has raised a lot of eyebrows is your use of partner surrogates—in other words, the treatment of unmarried patients with the help of partners who were unknown to them prior to the therapy.

M: Yes. We had 13 partner surrogates whom we used in the treatment of 41 unmarried men. Our dilemma in 1958 was "Do we take single men or women in treatment or do we not?" Following our concept of psychotherapy, we needed both male and female present for effective treatment, so our decision was either to take them and treat them with replacement partners and/or partner surrogates or not to take them at all. Our decision to go ahead was based on the fact that the research was committed to techniques that would work. I think the statistics over the 11 years have established unequivocally the value of the partner surrogate, and the story is something like this: There were 54 men and three women who, over an 11-year period, have been referred to the foundation for treatment of sexual dysfunction by their own local authorities, with the authorities well aware of the steps to be taken at the foundation. The three women came with their own selected partners, which we call replacement partners. Of the 54 men, 13 brought replacement partners, who were treated as if they were man and wife as far as the program was concerned; that left us with 41 males who required partner surrogates. There were 13 partner surrogates who were used for these 41 males. One of the partner surrogates is a female physician who volunteered for the role in order to evaluate it, for herself *and* for us. She continued to work with us on several occasions for about three years and has made a very real contribution to the techniques and use of the partner surrogate.

Q: Were there mores in 1958 that prevented you from doing some things then which you perhaps might do now?

M: Well, in 1958 there was no such thing as a comfortable, informative discussion of sexual functioning in any medical school in this country.

Q: How would your program be different if you were to begin in 1970?

M: That's a tough question.

Q: I mean, for instance, the surrogate.

M: We would continue using partner surrogates. It might be more acceptable today than it was in 1958.

J: Speculatively only, I think there's far less shock. I can't know how many people are going to have an intake of breath or be totally disapproving of our use of surrogates, but I certainly think the numbers would be far less today than in 1958. Human need tends to pre-empt blind rejection today.

M: You see, 11 of these 13 women had previously been married. None of them were married during the periods that they worked with us. I think there were actually 31 women who volunteered for this particular opportunity.

J: Their participation might be considered playing a role, essentially, a role which provided the crucial factor of social and physical interaction.

M: Yes, it is a role and the selectivity on our part was very high. All of them had major, significant reasons for wanting to work in this area. Those who came with some idea of "Gee, this would be interesting" were obviously eliminated in short order. The people we eventually chose were usually motivated by some experience in their own lives. Three of them had their marriages dissolved as a result of their husbands' sexual difficulties, and others had brothers or sisters with sexual difficulties, and so on. They are fine people. This was in no sense a prostitute population.

Q: How did you pair the patient with the surrogate?

J: There were a lot of factors to be considered. This society places great value on the male's sexual effectiveness—and for mostly the right reasons. So when this effectiveness is impaired, a great deal is in jeopardy, not just a man's ability to go to bed with a woman, but rather a sense of personal identity which, when conveyed by manner, word or deed, can become his identity in the eyes of his fellow man. Consequently, he comes with a highly motivated desire to have something done. Fortunately, I feel, society is moving toward a similar honorable role for female sexual expression (beyond the woman's reproductive anatomy, that is), and her motivation to reverse any sexual dysfunction will have a similar social reinforcement. Remember, we're talking in general terms and not about particular individuals of either sex. For most men, the partner surrogate is someone who understands and can help, not someone with whom they will spend the rest of their lives. But even if this were a social situation and not one as crucial as it is, rare is the individual, male or female, who sets out a protocol of requirements. Rarely do they think in terms of "Well, I might marry this person; therefore she must be blonde, five-foot-three; she must have a voice pitched in this decibel level; she must do this and this and this." Therefore, the requirements considered in the selection of partner surrogates are based far more on compassion, knowledge, regard and concern.

M: Within the realm of educational standards, such things as the cultural background of the individual and general attractiveness were examined carefully.

J: But attractiveness is relative, and we do, of course, have the histories of the patients as well as that of the partner surrogate to help in making a decision. The one common denominator that they all have, as women, is great value and great pleasure in their own sexual identity. This is the one thing we consider mandatory; this is the one thing that is real which they share. Beyond that, they're diverse in personality and in motivations. Some women just have such high regard for sexual expression as an enhancing factor of living that they think it is ghastly for some man to be ineffective if he can be helped.

M: Yes, I think that is probably the one important factor that should be mentioned. Each and every one of these partner surrogates has real security in her own sexual effectiveness, and as a result she has had real compassion for the male counterpart who did not.

Q: The male played no active role in the selection of a partner?

M: Absolutely not. This was done purely by Mrs. Johnson.

Q: Didn't you say in the book that you don't allow a surrogate to serve that function more than once a year?

M: That's about right. Approximately once a year.

Q: How many of those single men got married?

M: I'm not sure . . . about 24 out of 32.

Q: They never married the surrogate, though?

M: Nobody ever married the surrogate.

Q: What happens when the unmarried patient gets home?

M: Even before he is accepted as a patient, he must have established some opportunity to continue functioning in an effective sexual manner when he leaves us.

Q: But these people oftentimes don't have a partner because of their sexual dysfunction. . . .

M: It has been our experience that partners are available when the man returns relieved of his sexual dysfunction.

J: Stop and inspect the motivation necessary for the man to want to do this. He has identified his readiness and desire for marriage—many of these men had been divorced by their wives *because* of their dysfunction, and they are not about to involve another woman—who is usually waiting in the wings—unless they can be sure of their effectiveness.

M: But they don't want her to know about their sexual dysfunction.

J: Or, even if she knows, they don't want her to have to contend with it.

It may be splitting hairs, but I want to add something.

We are first, last and always a research entity. We have experimented in order to find a way to make things work. We are not in any sense seeking to say to society, "This is what you must do; this is how you must think." Within our research format, we so far have identified no other way to systematically reverse sexual dysfunction for the single male than with the use of partner surrogates. The same thing in theory would apply to the dysfunctional single female. Since the question hasn't been asked, I'll ask it for you. Why do we not use male partner surrogates for the female? Because as far as we have been able to discern by patient interrogation, it does not fit in with the value systems of most women. At present, the female, in general, does not have the same concept of her sexual role—is not allowed by society to place the same value upon her sexual expression—as the male. To oversimplify, the male in this society is allowed to honor his sexuality, his sexual effectiveness. We wish the male's sexual attitude were shared by all females. It is not. Even with freedom of communication, even with the far less rigid attitudes existing today, even with the real determination by many women to adopt comparably unfettered attitudes, female sexual responsivity is still a product of the residuals of older value systems. Only an unfortunately small percentage of girls and women who have given finite histories to us over the past 14 years seem to have avoided society's restricting influences. To briefly define the sexual value system, which is what I'm talking about, it addresses itself to those things which make response happen. They are very individual things or combinations of things which have been invested with sexual meaning and translate into erotic stimuli. Primarily, a woman who cannot honor her sexuality for its own sake has to develop some form of self-permission. Some females build a bridge from "dishonorable and unnatural" to "honorable and natural." But those who use a bridge from "dishonorable" to "forbidden" to "erotic" stimulation are delimiting their range of natural responsiveness. Now, permission has always had a great deal of resiliency and a great deal of individuality: I love him or he loves me; therefore I may be sexual. He is kind; therefore I may be sexual. Or I belong to him; therefore I may be sexual. Oh, the list could go on and on and vary from time to time, but the point is that there is still a great deal of complexity involved in most females' sexual value systems. Those things which turn her on must help her bridge the gap between "sex is dirty," "nice girls don't do it," etc., etc., and some assurance of a positive kind of investment in her own sexuality, her own sexual identity, in order to make it work for her. Well, we couldn't be so presumptive as to think we could produce men who would provide exactly those things, or to believe that at the screening level we could even define the things needed by a particular woman, or to presume that these things could be provided by a man chosen for her or that the woman herself could adapt her requirements. To further explore the situation, let's venture into a theoretical realm in which the therapist, who, out of his concept of good intent and responsibility to his female patient, decides to become the partner surrogate. Let's assume that his investment stops there, however. He is *not* available for marriage; he is *not* available for continuity of living or continuity of reinforcement on *any* basis. All right, so a reversal of symptoms may be achieved with him, but that's it, and most women usually require a lot more. In other words, few women seem to have sufficiently simple common denominators in their sexual value systems.

M: Now, emphasizing the fact that the decision about partner surrogates for women was made in 1958, and certainly we stuck to it for the period of statistical control, that does not mean to say that we might not change our minds as sexual functioning for the human female becomes more acceptable.

J: But we would still have to define in our own minds, from a sense of responsibility for the patient, whether or not she had come to value her sexual responsivity within a supporting pattern of other values.

THERAPIST SEDUCTION

M: To get back to what Gini just said about the therapist being his own surrogate, you always wonder in the back of your mind, "Gee, that was awful nice of him to help that poor girl. What did *he* get out of it?" And it isn't just the therapist and the girl that we're screaming about, as you can tell from the text. Granted, the female patient and male therapist is the most frequent duo, but we have recorded cases of the female therapist seducing male patients. We have recorded cases of male therapists seducing male patients into homosexuality, female therapists seducing female patients into Lesbianism, and this does not in any sense confine itself to medicine. I want that understood completely. It includes the psychologist, the social worker, the minister, priest and rabbi and various other professional disciplines. You name them, we've had them identified to us. We think it's time to blow the whistle, and we've done that in the text.

Q: Do you feel that the professional associations should take action?

M: I don't think it's up to us to set this in motion.

Q: There are some therapists who do this and admit doing it and claim it's healthy for the patient. How do you feel about that?

J: Within a patient's value system that does not approve such activity, it cannot be presumed to be effective or enhancing.

M: I would also like to point out to you that these seductive therapists are not individuals who are treating both husband and wife.

Q: How do you discourage something like that?

M: We don't really have to worry about it with a dual-sex team.

J: It takes two to engage in a seduction. If you do not accept —and this can be done without making the patient feel rejected—if, by introducing objectivity and perspective, you do not accept the seductive invitation and you help everyone define the goals and let them know patient-therapist intimacy is just not appropriate to the goals of an effective marriage, the seduction won't happen. If they are simply looking for available sex partners, rather than coming to the foundation for their stated reasons, they don't belong with us.

Q: Has it been the therapist seducing the patient or the patient seducing the therapist?

M: It's gone both ways.

J: One has to presume that both were available.

M: Both were obviously available. There is an occasional case, such as the therapist sneaking up on the patient's blind side, or the seduction of a young male into homosexuality, but I would guess most of the patients were hunting for some manner of support, and the therapist obviously made him or herself available.

Q: The patient must be very vulnerable, obviously.

J: Well, this is why the responsibility, I feel, has to be placed on the therapist, because the patient is a vulnerable individual, an individual in need, who has come presumably with the intention of getting help.

THERAPY PATIENTS

Q: One of the criticisms of your first book was that your sample was not representative. What about your new sample?

M: It's just as skewed. In the first place, it's certainly not a cross section of the population in terms of educational background or in terms of socioeconomic background. You must remember, also, that these patients are *referred*. We do not allow ourselves the opportunity of direct patient application; we work only with those who are referred to us.

J: Probably the single most crucial factor in our failure to have a broad spectrum of patients is the self-selective factor. In other words, people who seek the treatment are motivated, and this in itself tends to bias the population.

Q: You're undoubtedly going to be charged with rejecting the hard cases and taking the easy cases to swell your success rate or reduce your failure rate.

J: There's a simple answer to that—the fact is that other therapists don't refer their easy cases.

M: Let me give you an example. Let's suppose that fundamentally we have a referral of a male who is in a state of acute alcoholism. Why come to St. Louis at that stage of the game? We would refer him to a local physician, to bring the alcoholism under control, after which his problems of sexual inadequacy may also respond. This is the type of screening we do.

TREATMENT FOLLOW-UP

Q: And what about your follow-up? You interview after how long a time?

M: During the first year, frequent follow-up is a vital part of maintaining positive therapeutic results. We schedule a follow-up communication between four and a half and five and a half years after treatment and call it our five-year termination interview. I think this is the first time that five-year follow-up has been recorded in psychotherapy. Up to this time the statistics presented have been based on the termination of the acute-treatment phase for the problem. But the acute-treatment phase might be very long or very brief, and no one knows what happens after the patient leaves the therapist. So we felt that a long-range control period was in order—that is, if we were going to present a new concept of rapid treatment, then we must be able to support this concept with some objectivity. So we deliberately set out to establish a system of five-year follow-up. If the therapy is of value, then inevitably there should be a relatively small reversal in the five years following treatment. And we felt that we should talk only in terms of failures and that we should evaluate our failures not only during the acute phase of therapy but for five years after termination. Someone said, "Why haven't you gone for ten?" and the answer is perhaps we should have, but there's only so much time.

Q: If I understand you correctly, any reversal that occurred after the intensive period and during this five-year follow-up was included as a failure.

M: That's correct.

Q: Then, why are you unwilling to do the same thing with successes that occurred as a result of treatment but happened after the patient left your clinic?

J: Some within 24 hours after they left.

M: Well, the reason is this: We wanted to present statistics that any other treatment center could equal or surpass; so we prejudiced the statistics as much as possible. In other words, we wanted to make sure that this technique would not be regarded as something that was limited, selected or difficult to reproduce. We would expect over a period of time a better return than ours for most treatment centers.

Q: Yes, but it might have been hopeful information for other therapists to learn that even though they failed to produce results during the acute-treatment period, there was still a chance for reversal of symptoms later on.

J: Very good point.

M: As a matter of fact, this is described in the text. There are possibilities for reversal later on, and often they were so reported, but we did not claim them as treatment successes.

J: You're very right in tuning in on that, because the very nature of the intensely hopeful approach for two weeks carries with it a great potential of positive return subsequent to the treatment period.

Q: What percentage of your couples have returned for a second course?

M: Very few. Eight or nine have returned. Actually, I'm sure there would have been more returns but we felt we might be keeping them from other forms of psychotherapy perhaps more appropriate for them.

Q: At what age is therapy most effective?

M: Generally speaking, the older the patient, the higher the failure rate.

Q: What do you define as aging?

M: Anything over 50. Let me add that relatively few older people were referred. However, our failure rate in the aging population was about one out of three, or 33 percent. Our over-all failure rate was 20 percent. Despite the fact that our failure rate with the aging is one out of three, I think this is an incredibly hopeful statistic. In the past, people have never tried to treat the aging male or female for sexual dysfunction. The basic concept was that nothing could be done. Even if in our clumsy way—and it is clumsy at this stage of the game—we are failing a third of the time, this is infinitely better than not trying at all.

Q: A couple of years ago you said that a few psychotics had slipped through the screening process—people whom you felt were just too disturbed to work with. Have you softened your position on that? Are you working with severely disturbed people? Or where do you draw the line?

M: We draw the line at the level of the major psychoses. In other words, the same sort of restriction level that psychoanalysis would have. We do not deal with those patients who are contending with major psychoses, even though they may have sexual dysfunctions. This is an area in which they need total professional psychiatry. We are more and more being asked to work with these individuals in conjunction with psychotherapeutic control by psychiatry. But represented in the present text are no specifically defined psychoses.

PSYCHIATRIC CRITICISM

Q: While we're talking about psychotherapy, how do you feel about the criticism that your therapy merely treats symptoms and allows the underlying psychological problem to remain untouched?

M: Sometimes this is true, and often it probably is not. The logical thing to do, of course, is to refer the patient for intensive psychotherapy—if he or she needs it. But there's no need for that patient to carry a curable sexual distress with him or her before or during treatment for the underlying problem. Frequently, you know, the symptom *creates* additional problems, and the removal of that symptom could make psychotherapy easier. But I'm just speculating. I'm not a psychiatrist.

Q: Do your patients treat their new-found sexual function like a toy? I can just see one of them saying, "Hey, I've been to the clinic," and flaunting his new virility to all the ladies on the block.

M: One thing that people—especially men—don't talk about is where they have been, because they don't want to describe the fact that they were sexually dysfunctional to start with. They go to great pains to make sure people don't know what they are doing. They don't come back and brag about it. It isn't like showing off a new baby.

DUAL DYSFUNCTION

Q: How often, when you're dealing with a couple, are both of them dysfunctional?

M: Forty-four percent of the time the difficulty is on both sides of the fence, but the referring authority rarely says so. The husband is being sent because he's a premature ejaculator. But no one knows whether the wife is nonorgasmic or not, or vice versa.

Q: So you treat two for the price of one?

M: Yes.

Q: Is that more difficult?

M: Not necessarily. Except for the fact that we develop the therapy progression a little faster and we have to concentrate on the male first.

J: The wife does require something with which to work, which the husband first must be able to provide.

M: To oversimplify it, the first week belongs to the male.
The second week is the female's.

DOCTOR SELF-REFERRAL

*Q: I was interested in the number of doctors who were under
treatment at the center as part of your study. I assume some
of them come about through self-referral.*
M: They all do.
Q: Could you give your general impressions of these men?
M: I can only say that these are men and women with sexual
dysfunctions. Seventeen and one half percent of our total
number of patients were in the category of self-referral. Of
this group, 48 percent had been trained in psychiatry. I think
this only represents the fact that these people know where
to refer themselves. Rather than assume that they, as a profession, have an unusually high rate of sexual distress, it is
more appropriate to presume that they have a high regard for
the quality of sexual effectiveness. They send patients and
then send themselves eventually. Sometimes they send themselves and then send patients. It goes both ways. But they
do have, with their particular disciplinary exposure, more
opportunity to know what's going on.
J: We've been asked if they ever come in order to learn the
techniques so they can apply them to their patients. Well,
yes, to a greater or lesser degree, the technique and the
attitude stay with them. Many of them do communicate
the fact that they are now doing their own adaptation of
our therapy.
*Q: Their kind of dysfunction was no different from that of
the rest of your patients?*
M: No.

PRIOR PSYCHIATRIC CARE

*Q: You said in your book that those with experience in
psychotherapy could usually talk more about sex but they
had to learn to feel it.*
M: That's right. Forty-four percent of those who were referred to us had had some prior form of psychotherapeutic
treatment. This group was easy to work with because they
could talk and answer questions and give a very vivid history
much more freely and effectively than those who had not

been exposed to psychotherapy. It's a double-edged sword, though, because you find with many married couples that the husband or wife who had been exposed to psychotherapy wanted to be in the spotlight. So we had difficulty in balancing.

J: These are people who had been in psychotherapy for many years usually.

Q: Isn't it true that many doctors—I'm talking about physicians—are also used to being in the spotlight? This is their usual posture. Wasn't it difficult to treat them?

J: Not necessarily. They learned to be patients. It doesn't take very long. Sometimes the transition is highlighted by a bit of a clash. You know, like who is taking care of whom. But it's brief. It only requires a reminder.

M: I'd say the great leveler is the physical examination. Once they've had that, they know who the patient is.

DUAL-SEX THERAPY

Q: You've already discussed the dual-sex team—the man and woman who perform the therapy—and you've mentioned it in the book, too. Do you consider this absolutely essential for your kind of treatment?

M: Absolutely.

Q: As the cotherapists work together over a period of time, does it become easier for one of them to understand the subtleties of the other sex?

M: Yes, indeed. Actually, you begin to finish each other's sentences.

Q: You're approaching, perhaps, the first dialogue between the sexes.

J: I'm delighted that you made that point, because as far as we are concerned, it's one of the single most interesting returns from the program. The fact that men and women together, in teams of two, have been able to communicate effectively in achieving common goals, without loss of mutual regard or self-esteem, seems to be unique.

Q: Do you have male-female competition, or role playing, among therapists?

J: It's potential. . . .

M: What we really try to do in the therapy is to have the male represent the male at all times and the female represent the female. If there were two males, the patient's husband and myself, for instance, one trying to tell her what was wrong or trying to interpret her problems, she'd have little security. And she wouldn't be sure she was getting across a woman's point of view to two men.

Q: You therapists change partners, so to speak, so you don't have the same teams working together all the time?

J: Correct.

Q: If I understand you, you are saying that for the first time you are producing men who really understand women sexually. . . .

M: No, we're producing men who know damn well they *don't* understand women.

J: And are willing to accept a woman's interpretation of *herself* as a woman. The fact that more than 95 percent of all the interpretations and definitions of female sexuality and responsivity have been produced by men is something that I personally reject—and not on a feminist basis at all. I simply reject it because the content is often inaccurate.

M: Well, we can't reject all the content, because some of it may well have value. But the point is, the individual males who have written about female sexuality have been insecure in their statements. I think it has been tragic that almost everything that has been written about female sexual function has been written by males. If our laboratory has established something of value in the last 16 years, it's that the male conceptualizes female sexual functioning very poorly, and vice versa.

SEXUAL VALUE SYSTEM

J: Of course, women often have to be willing to accept a male interpretation of themselves—not the male who says, "I know this is what you want, dear," but rather who says, "Who are you? What do you need? How do you feel?" And that brings me to another truism of this mode of psychotherapy, and that is that we never impose a value system upon a pair of patients—marital partners—that is foreign to their own. In other words, we function within the context of *their* life style, their value systems, and most pertinent, we help them define their *own* individual sexual value system. It is from this that their responsivity and effectiveness is developed, not anything we say such as "This is what you need" or "This is how you should achieve it."

Q: You mentioned the sexual value system in the book. Would you elaborate on it, please?

J: Well, we found that the things which have sexual connotation for a particular person are highly individual. It is never the same set of things among different people, and often the pattern is variable in one individual from situation to situation. In other words, sexual requirements may be altered by other values operating in a particular situation or at a particular time. In the history taking, it is often possible to define many of those things to which an individual has been able to respond sexually. Or, if he or she has never reached a level of effective response, you can define those things which are embodied in the individual's expectations, fantasies, dreams, hopes or speculative thought processes. To give you an example: In defining the sexual value system, you elicit a definition of those sensations and circumstances which are remembered as being physically and/or sexually stimulating, exciting, desirable and enhancing. Then you try to ascertain how acceptable the individual finds these things. In other words, having identified them, can he or she accept them when offered to the point where they are translatable into sexual expression when given the opportunity by a partner? Are they desirable only in fantasy or are they truly something that is meaningful? And what of the world around the individual? What does it say is right or wrong, and how much does the individual accept of society's judgments? The sexual value system is that which turns one on. In short, it's the remembered warmth of touch or word or deed—anything that can be responded to in a positive way. It need not be necessarily sexual in its direct connotation, because there are many layers surrounding sexual responsivity that move and lead up to it. Anything that sets in motion the remembered desire to be with another person or to communicate physically is part of it, and it translates in succession up to that which actually deals with the physical, sexual interaction.

M: Let me give you an application of this concept. There is a woman who came with her husband to St. Louis, who said that we failed her. She had a totally cooperative husband whom she loved very much. She was very close to orgasm on many occasions and completely frustrated, and so was he and so were we. In the two-week therapy, we failed. As is true for people who come for treatment, we work around the wife's menstrual cycle. So, after two weeks at the clinic, we can anticipate the imminence of another period. Well, very quietly I said to the husband in a very brief moment before they left, "I want to make a suggestion to you. After you have gotten home and are reoriented, wait for two or three days after her menstrual period is over, until about the time that your wife is beginning to wonder when you'll be resuming sex. Then, one morning on the way to work, just stop at the door, look her right in the eye and say, 'Get a lot of rest this afternoon; you're going to need it!' Don't say anything more, just leave." He did this and next thing I knew, the phone rang about 1:30 in the morning with somebody crying and somebody laughing and everybody pleased as punch. It happened just as expected. The therapy had been done, the background was there, the knowledge was there, the desire was there. But she somehow needed a bridge between them all. And when he looked her right in the eye and said, "Get a lot of rest this afternoon," that was it. She had the kids farmed out and she had his favorite meal ready. She greeted him at the door with practically nothing on, and it worked—for her.

J: But this may not work for someone else. And that is why we stress so strongly the uniqueness of each individual's sexual value system. Why do we put the sexual value system in the female chapter rather than the male? Because the male, by social mores and by very practical, realistic requirements, is allowed to *honor* his sexuality—he may grow up in the most rigid of circumstances; yet he is still expected to be sexually effective at all times. The female is not. When the marriage vows are said, she is supposed, by some divine guidance, to become an effective person sexually. But when she is developing bases for sexuality, they frequently are wrenched away from her by social restrictions. You know, nice girls don't do it. If a child asks innocent questions like "When will I be able to have babies?" or, later, "Why do I feel sensations in certain places?" mamma in embarrassment says, "Oh, you're too young to think about that." She may get the back of the hand and go sailing across the room or she may notice red-faced confusion in her mother's manner. In other words, the feelings that are developing when she says, "Why do I feel thus and so?" are absolutely wrenched from her by various forms of rejection. No one says, "This is a part of growing up; this is a part of your future as a woman; this is something that will be enhancing when used with appropriate understanding and control." And that's the point. You can *allow* natural sexual development in the context of acceptable social mores. You don't have to say thou shalt not, it is dirty, it is bad, it is objectionable. You *can* control it and still let it develop naturally. Society may expect certain behavior in the expression of sexual identity, but it need not reject the fact of that sexual identity. A child could be taught to recognize it, think on it, dream on it, plan for it. But that's not the way young women generally are brought up. They are taught one way or another that sexual feelings should be suppressed while they dream and talk about romantic things. Their thoughts of marriage are directed toward selection of a husband on an economic basis, on a social basis, but that which represents mutual sexual values is left to be stumbled upon without anticipation or information.

THERAPY CLINICS

Q: May we return to the therapists? Is there a possibility of a network of sexual-dysfunction clinics with Masters-and-Johnson-trained therapists?

M: I don't know. But what we plan, if we can finance it, is development of a training program. We are hoping to start this in the next academic year. We have applications of over 200 dual-sex teams cleared and waiting for training. We just haven't been able to swing the thing financially, but if we can, we plan to train senior representatives from the various medical and behavorial centers, let them go back to their own areas and start training there. Whether this is going to work or not, we don't know.

J: What we plan doesn't involve merely training in our specific techniques, but our concepts and what they represent, so that adaptations can be made in the interest of further clinical research in psychotherapy.

Q: Would each team have a physician?

M: We would hope that there would be a biologist—or M.D.—and a behaviorist in each group at this stage of the program. And we don't care whether the female is the M.D. and the male is the behaviorist or vice versa. And if two M.D.s wish to team up, that's all right, too.

Q: But you won't pair up anybody. It will be a team from the same city who plan to work together, won't it?

M: That's the idea; they will go back to their own center and do further training.

J: The requests that we've had generally have come from people who accept our concept that there should be a man-woman, multidiscipline combination; they have put themselves together as teams.

Q: Have you screened the list—the 200 sex teams you mentioned?

M: Yes.

J: There has been quite an exchange of correspondence or telephone calls.

M: This has gone on for two and a half years now.

Q: And all that stands between you and training these men and women is money?

M: That's correct, and the time and professional help that money provides.

Q: So, as some therapists are known as Freudians, these would be known as Masters-Johnson disciples.

J: No, we don't have any labels for this.

M: These would be known simply as boys and girls.

FINANCES

Q: You've mentioned finances, or the lack of them, several times. Just how do you finance your laboratory?

M: Well, there's our first book, *Human Sexual Response.* One third of the income from that goes to myself, one third to Mrs. Johnson, and one third to the foundation, which is as much as the government would allow us to give.

Q: Would you care to say how much the book made?

M: I wouldn't care to say. We simply can tell you that the book has sold over 300,000 copies, at ten dollars per copy.

Q: Can you name some of the foundations that have contributed to your operation?

M: No, we don't have their permission, but I will say that private foundations provide us with a large measure of support.

Q: Why don't you apply to the Playboy Foundation?

M: The Playboy Foundation is supporting us generously.

Q: Do you have federal support?

M: We do not.

Q: Several years ago, you had a grant from the government.

M: That's right. It was $25,000 a year for four years.

Q: And then in 1963, hoping to expand your work, you applied to the National Institute of Mental Health for a much larger grant. You didn't get it and you lost the smaller sum that you had been receiving.

M: That is correct.

Q: How much did you apply for?

M: Well, it started at about $250,000 a year and expanded from there on for a seven-year period. The total thing was denied.

Q: Have you since then applied for any federal funds?

M: We have talked on two occasions to the Institute of Child Health and Human Development, and these have been only in conversational stages, but application was discouraged.

Q: Why?

M: Uh . . . that's up to them.

Q: Do you think that's a wise policy?

M: I wouldn't dream of criticizing their policy. I mean this very seriously. It's not up to an applicant to criticize their policies, and I happen to believe very strongly that NIMH is exquisitely fair about their grants. We were simply turned down. That's their privilege and their responsibility, and there's no sour grapes whatsoever.

J: It might be of some interest to you to know that at the time this program project grant was turned down, we had applied shortly before that for a construction grant.

M: Yes, we got matching-fund grants for a quarter of a million dollars, which we had at the time from private sources, to build our physical plant.

J: Well, we didn't accept the government matching aid.

M: Yes, when NIMH would not offer us support in running the facility, we returned the private funds, and then the matching federal grant was not forthcoming.

Q: Has any contributor ever given you funds with strings attached?
M: Never. We have had money offered for restricted use that we have declined. But those who have helped to support us have attached no strings whatsoever.

Q: You didn't mention patient fees as part of your finances.
M: Excuse me. The full patient fee is $2500. About 50 percent of the patients pay that. Twenty-five percent are given free care. This means total free care. This is not like the hospital story today where there is no such thing as free care. Another 25 percent pay an adjusted fee of our basic cost. The two weeks of intensive therapy plus five years of follow-up cost us $1250. This is what these patients pay.

Q: Does that include the rental of hotels?
M: No, it does not.

J: We do negotiate with local hotels or apartment hotels to make available at a minimum cost a pleasant place where the patients can do their own cooking. But there are people who make their own reservations and take suites in the leading hotels. Others prefer to avail themselves of these negotiated rentals.

Q: Do you have any adjustment on your fees if there's a failure?
M: No. We have many times arbitrarily decided not to charge, but we are not bound to such an arrangement.

Q: Do your free patients have as much success as your paying clients?
J: Yes, they do. I know why you're asking that question— because of the expected lower motivation that accompanies free care. But in this case, you see, they still have the cost of the stay in St. Louis, plus the cost of travel.

Q: What is the foundation budget per year?
M: Approximately a half million—give or take ten percent.

Q: Why, now that you are a household name, will you not reapply to the federal government?
M: I didn't say we wouldn't. It would have to be under certain circumstances. We couldn't use government funds to do certain types of research because our study subjects would have to be identified. But there are certainly other types of funding. For instance, they might find acceptable a postgraduate training program.

Q: What other kinds of research are you doing?

M: We are interested in starting a much more sophisticated type of work. We're interested in doing neurophysiology in the Seventies, and that requires a whole new laboratory. We have, for instance, done all of the physiology of homosexual functioning, and this has been done now for almost two years but will not be reported until the mid-Seventies. At this stage, where we have established our basic concepts of natural sexual functioning in the various categories, the whole lab has to be reconstituted, and we are in the process of trying to raise the money to do this.

Q: Do you plan to do cardiovascular work?

M: We certainly do. This would be all a part of our neurophysiology. With the same type of instrumentation, we could do the cardiorespiratory work. Again, it's a matter of financing. You see, the difficulty is that a physiology laboratory maintained at the level that we are talking about would certainly cost at least $100,000 a year to maintain. We don't have that kind of money at this stage.

J: And unlike the clinical applications of our work, this type of research would have no financial returns. It cannot sustain itself.

M: You see, the biochemical laboratory can't support itself. The clinical treatment programs can. And hopefully the postgraduate training programs can maintain themselves once established, but when it comes to a physiology laboratory, that's all output, and it's very difficult to find that kind of money in any consistency. When someone says, "All right, I'll give you a grant for the year," it wouldn't help a bit, because these are long-range programs.

FOUNDATION STAFF

Q: With this truly ambitious program of yours, do you get much time for yourselves?

M: We work a seven-day week 11 months a year. We don't accept any cases in December. We've done this since 1954. And will continue to do so. There are five professional members of the staff at this time. The disciplines represented are biochemistry, the ministry, psychology, sociology and gynecology. Psychiatry will be with us late in 1970.

Q: These are other members of the staff, or are you including yourselves?
M: These are including ourselves.

TOTAL PROGRAM

Q: Before we get any deeper into the background of your new book, may I ask you a question about your old one? Specifically, I believe there must be a connection between Human Sexual Response *and* Human Sexual Inadequacy, *but the connection isn't obvious to me. Can you guide us through that?*
M: Well, the total program in investigating sexual response is predicated on learning in the laboratory—the first book—applying what you have learned clinically—the new book—and then finally moving to preventive medicine—the subject of future books. We hope to allot a decade to each of these programs, and we start a new program about every five years. So in the mid-Fifties—1954—we worked in the laboratory investigating the physiology and anatomy of sexual response. The project for the Sixties was this therapy program that is just being released. The statistical-control period for human sexual inadequacy started in January 1959 and terminated in December 1969, so that was another decade. In the mid-Sixties we started working on our third project, which is the investigation of human homosexual functioning. This will be released hopefully sometime in the mid-Seventies. Finally, we are just in the process of initiating our program for the decade of the Seventies which has to do with preventive medicine. In the course of the next decade, we would like to come up with some concepts of how to *avoid* sexual dysfunction rather than just treat it. This is the program in a nutshell.

Q: But is there any progressive connection between what you learn in the lab and what you are doing in the rapid-treatment program? Or simply a question of eliminating one before you go into the other?
J: The total program has always been thought of as having two tracks: One is the laboratory and the other is the clinical application of laboratory findings. This new book essentially reflects more of the psychosocial aspects which emerged concomitantly with the original physiological and anatomical

findings, and we felt that the material would be more usable, more pertinent, if placed and highlighted within a clinical format. So it was an arbitrary choice not to do a book on the psychology or the psychosocial aspects of sexual response that technically would have been a matching piece to the first book, on physiology and anatomy. But rather we chose to take these findings and place them in the more meaningful clinical context.

M: I really think that this text should go a long way toward removing a significant amount of the criticism which was based on the concept that, after all, ours is just a laboratory research program—that we were mechanistic. Few people ever bothered to read the first text carefully enough to notice that we said we were using the laboratory as a springboard for the development of effective clinical therapy—as well as scientific fact to replace mythology. We could have turned these statistics loose four or five years ago when the screams of anguish developed, but we would have destroyed our five-year follow-up.

TEXT READERSHIP

Q: Whom was this text written for?

M: Hopefully, it is directed to those who provide therapy for sexual dysfunction. The discipline that does the greatest amount of such therapy is of religious orientation. More patients are treated by clergymen than by any other group. Next would be social scientists—the clinical psychologist, the social worker, the marriage counselor. The discipline that is a very poor third in terms of numbers of cases would be medicine. So, inevitably, this text was not written purely for physicians.

Q: What about the public itself? Can the lay individual find your book useful?

M: We think so. Though I'll never understand why the public tried to read the first book. I had a hell of a time reading it myself. In *Human Sexual Inadequacy* there would be certain advantages in the general public reading it, but I would want to make it absolutely clear that this is not a how-to-do-it book in any sense of the word.

Q: Well, if it's not a how-to book, why should the public bother plunking down $12.50 for it?

M: I think that people with sexual distress might develop a hopeful approach to their problem if they read the book. I think it would give them some understanding that therapy doesn't have to take years and, too, that most sexual distresses are not hopelessly difficult to reverse. These are approaches that they might pick up from the text. And, you know, an individual who has a sexual problem is convinced that he is, if not the only one, then one of a few who have ever had anything so horrible. It would be extremely healthy to let him know what a widespread concern there is about sexual dysfunction. It might also give him courage, finally, to approach someone and ask for help.

RELIGIOUS ORTHODOXY

Q: There is a constantly repeated implication in your book that one of the reasons for the sexual distresses you write about is religious orthodoxy.
M: There is no question about it. Unequivocally, absolutely, religious orthodoxy is responsible for a significant degree of sexual dysfunction. And it doesn't matter which of the three major religions is involved.
Q: Have you noticed any differences in sexual dysfunction according to ethnic grouping?
M: We don't have a big enough population on which to base a comparative statement.
Q: Can you undo in two weeks, or even in your five-year follow-up, what religious orthodoxy has done from childhood up through the marriage?
M: The answer is yes, we do, and sometimes no, we don't. It's very resistant.
J: It normally depends on the quality of motivation. There is hope if the partners see effective sexual function as something to be valued, if they see its absence as something debilitating. And there's hope if they have come to realize that the rigidity of their early influence is perhaps a little too intense. You see, they don't have to *reject* their religion in order to shed some of the rigidity of the early teachings. I recollect no one who has thrown out his basic religious beliefs in order to take on a new set of rules that allow him to become sexually functional; rather, I think, they put the

rigidity in perspective in the face of their high degree of motivation.

SEX AND ALCOHOL

Q: In your book, you also single out alcohol as a primary cause of sexual dysfunction.

M: I do not suggest that alcohol *inevitably* leads to sexual dysfunction. I am talking about individual sensitivity to it not only between individuals, but in the same individual from time to time. Certainly, it's true that one of the great causes of secondary impotence is an acute alcoholic episode. Statistically, that was way up on the list, but there is many a man who has had entirely too much to drink, tried to have intercourse and failed, and said, "Gee, that was just because I had too much to drink." He then went on about his business and it never bothered him a bit. So I want to stress it isn't always cause and effect.

PREMATURE EJACULATION

Q: Don't you say in the book that premature ejaculation is a common cause of impotence?

M: Yes, indeed. It follows a pattern of the wife's misunderstanding of the husband's lack of ejaculatory control, which usually leads to increasing demands that he provide her with satisfaction. Failing to do so, he begins to doubt his potency and, sure enough, he eventually loses it.

Q: And don't you also mention that the cured premature ejaculator sometimes falls into the secondary-impotence syndrome?

J: Well, yes, sometimes a couple is so elated over their elimination of distress that they treat their new sexual function like a toy.

M: We always have to warn them about this. In the last chapter, on our therapeutic failures, we describe a situation that simply got away from us through our own fault entirely. The husband was a premature ejaculator whose problem was reversed and everything was just fine. So they went home and just wore this thing out, and he ultimately became secondarily impotent. He only needed one episode of secondary impotence—and his self-confidence wasn't that well established to start with—and before he knew it, the problem was chronic. So, if we have a premature ejaculator, we can cure him in a week, but, in truth, since we're treating the marital relationship and not just the premature ejaculation, we keep them longer and watch them carefully because it is not impossible to have an episode or two of erective difficulty in this process.

Q: Is it the wife who has to be cautioned?

M: No, they both have to be cautioned.

J: The specific case Bill is talking about relates to two people who are articulate, intelligent and rather well suited. The treatment worked for them in a short time and we rather naïvely let them go before the end of the two-week period. Everything was just fine and they were completely happy, but, of course, what we had failed to do was equip them with the knowledge of the nature of their own responsivity so that they could handle it adequately.

Q: What caused the erective inadequacy later? Was it demand from the wife or physiological depletion of the male?

M: Just physiological depletion. It was only in one episode, but here is a man who is already sensitized to fear his lack of performance from his premature ejaculation, and when the erective difficulty occurred, he needed knowledgeable reassurance. He and his wife thought it was the result of the treatment or something like that. It wasn't at all. But it scared them half to death.

Q: You've been quoted as saying that premature ejaculation won't be a problem in ten years. Is that an accurate assessment of your views?

M: I said if we had adequate training, premature ejaculation would disappear in ten years.

Q: Would you define premature ejaculation for us? There seems to be confusion in the medical profession about what exactly it is.

M: There certainly is confusion. I have never heard a good definition of premature ejaculation, and that includes our own. It's purely relative to the individual married couple. Going around the country, we ran into a definition at a medical school that had to do with a man ejaculating within 30 seconds of intromission. This gave me the image of a wife holding a stop watch and peering between numbers 29 and 31. Other definitions push the stop watch up to a minute. Well, time span really isn't the answer. A premature ejaculator, according to our view, is a man who doesn't have ejaculatory control sufficient to satisfy his partner in at least 50 percent of the opportunities. If his partner is nonorgasmic, of course, that shoots our definition full of holes. I guess premature ejaculation is really a state of mind within a particular marriage, because while it seems to depend on the female response, that response can vary from time to time.

J: Yes, but let's talk about male response. It would seem that, increasingly, men want to achieve this control because they consider it desirable for themselves, not just for the woman. There has been a tendency in discussing sex to focus on ejaculatory control for the purpose of fulfilling the female's need. But we've noted that men are beginning to reflect the feeling that their own experience is enhanced by their ability and facility to sustain the action.

M: That's true. As proof of that, in the last two years we've had an increasing number of couples who were referred because the husband said, "Let's do something about it." In the past, it was almost always the wife who demanded that something be done.

Q: The squeeze technique you use in premature ejaculation, it's not new, is it?

M: The technique of manipulation and stopping, manipulation, stopping was suggested by James Semans, a urologist. Also, the first suggestion that the wife could help orient her husband's control was made by Dr. Semans. The actual squeeze technique was introduced by us.

FEMALE ORGASM

Q: Some statistics show that a woman who achieves orgasm by any means, including a vibrator or masturbation, will have a better chance of achieving it with a man. Is this true in your experience?

J: I'm reluctant to discuss that here because it's a complicated subject. The question is under what circumstances can a particular woman translate her experience from one stimulus to another? The answer is complex and individual.

Q: In the therapy you put a lot of emphasis on the question of nondemand.

M: Well, the idea that you can demand an orgasm is one of the most distracting misconceptions that have ever been perpetrated. If you stop to think about the orgasmic experience—be it male or female—it is the ultimate expression of self to a progressive sequence of sexual stimuli.

J: You see, each level of stimuli leads to the next, involuntarily; so it's impossible to move toward a specific goal or performance by the numbers. You simply obviate the natural culmination of the experience. It no longer expresses the time, mood, circumstance and human need, but represents a challenge, a goal, a prescribed pattern instead of a natural, human experience. It's taking a natural function, a medium of human exchange, and subjecting it to rigid, formal kinds of requirements and demands.

M: Mutual orgasm, the great be-all and end-all of the marriage manuals, falls into this category. Now, if you stop to think about it physiologically, the human female has the capacity for multiorgasm, though that doesn't mean to say she always is multiorgasmic or always must be. The human male does not have that capacity—particularly much after the age of 30 or 35. We are talking averages now. If you are going to have mutual orgasm as the be-all and end-all, this simply means that the female has her orgasm once. But she may well be interested in more than one orgasm.

J: What makes orgasm a qualitative experience? Only end-point release? Or all that goes into arriving there? Should we impose a time schedule on it or let it be anything it wants?

Q: With all this talk about orgasm, you haven't used the word "frigidity" once. That's remarkable.

M: You won't find that word in the book, either, simply because we have no way of defining it. We have no concept of what frigidity means, and I'm sure if we asked everybody in the room to write us a definition, there would be as many definitions as people. It means entirely different things to husbands, to wives, to professionals, to all kinds of people. Example: If a wife is orgasmic once a week in a two- or three-times-a-week exposure, the husband might well send his wife to her gynecologist saying, "Treat her for her frigidity," and again, if the wife is never orgasmic, he might send her and say, "Take care of her frigidity," so it doesn't mean anything.

J: To me it sounds like something a group of men in the Victorian era dreamed up when they all retired from the company of women for their port and cigars.

SEX AND AGING

Q: Another belief which can be dated back to the Victorians —and perhaps beyond—is the idea that sex is only for the young. Your new book will probably put that notion to rest forever.

M: Well, we certainly hope so. The section having to do with sex and aging is probably as important as any other part of the book. Hopefully, once this information has been disseminated, society can eliminate the tragedy of men and women in the age group of 50 and beyond who talk themselves out of effective sexual functioning. We now know several physiological facts of aging that affect the sexual functioning, just as the physiological fact of aging affects every other physical process in the body. The aging male has several things happen to him. First, he has a reduction in seminal-fluid volume. Second, he is slower to erect. He's also slower to run around the block in his 60s than he was in his 20s, but that doesn't worry him. Yet the fact that it takes him a little longer to have an erection scares him to death. And the minute he becomes concerned—the minute the male develops any fears of performance—then he has trouble having an erection.

Other factors: He also loses some of his demand for ejaculation. I think this is probably the most important factor that we've discovered. If men and women in their 50s, 60s and 70s, and possibly 80s, go on with continuity of sexual functioning at, let's say, once or twice a week and the male ejaculates at *his* demand level, which in his 60s or 70s might be every ten days, he will *not* develop fears and he will not become secondarily impotent. We will, in fact, take the definitive stand that the aging process does not in any way interfere with the erective process into the 80-year age group unless it does so from acquired fears of performance which result from not understanding the physiological changes.

On the female side there are also certain factors to be considered. Once the woman has gone through the menopausal years, she is slower to lubricate. Lubrication and erection are absolutely parallel physiological processes, and the same tissues that produce erection in the male produce lubrication in the female.

J: I would like to insert the word *may* in reference to female lubrication.

M: Indeed, she *may* be slower to lubricate.

J: Or he *may* be slower to erect.

M: She also has some loss in vaginal sensitivity. She has lost the thickening of the lining of the vagina, and this may make intercourse irritating if it is just an occasional exposure. She has less chance of developing these reverses if she is maintained on steroid-replacement concepts, but whether or not she is on steroid replacement, these involutional changes cause very little distress if there is *continuity* of sexual exposure. But if it's once every six months, she'll have problems.

SEXUAL CONTINUITY

Q: This desirability of continuity, that doesn't apply just to old people does it? Isn't continuity of sexual function important at all ages?

M: Yes.

Q: But are you talking about a physical necessity or a frame of mind?

M: Certain physical problems relating to effective sexual functioning can arise as a result of sexual disuse. But essentially we're talking about a frame of mind. At a certain age, the male will have already talked himself into difficulties by telling himself, "This just isn't fitting; this just isn't proper. After all, I'm 65, and that's too old." But if the individual has a healthy continuity of sexual expression, it helps prevent him from accepting the general public's attitude against sex among the aged.

J: Let me give an example. Let's take newlyweds in their first year of marriage. Often, their whole concept of sexuality is that it is a man's world and she is to be lovingly available and loved in return for her availability. With the standard American attitude, she assumes that if she importunes at all, if she even moves toward him in any way, she will be labeled aggressive, unfeminine, etc. He, on the other hand,

may wonder if her manner implies that she is not desirous of any kind of sexual interaction. So he waits for a signal, she waits for a signal, and nothing happens. Now, this kind of lack of continuity has nothing to do with numbers. It has to do with the freedom to express or to be expressed to, to give and to take sexual expression. It doesn't necessarily lead to or make intercourse mandatory, per se, but rather it is a continuity of understanding and open exchange. Lacking this, each partner sends up a rigid signal, a kind of negative defense: "OK, if he doesn't want me, I don't care." The pattern becomes so well established, if they have done their job of pretending well, that eventually they don't *feel* anything. They become panic-stricken. "I don't feel anything. What's wrong with me? It's ended." So the nature of responsivity is something that's terribly hard to grasp for most people in the face of the myths and superstitions that have been laid down in great layers for so long. In truth, sex is an expression that really must be used. Bill has suggested that for the male, there is not such a heavy physical component. I accept the statement, but for the female, continuity of expression has a very real physical component, and it would relate to vaginal mucosa. Stimulated by sexual opportunity, it remains ready—in other words, responsive.
M: Yes, for instance, there are many cases of women who are sexually exposed regularly, and in the postmenopausal years they lubricate very well because of the continuity of expression. Now, if these same women were to stop functioning for four or five months in their early 60s, they might have trouble with lubrication for a good while when they resumed.
J: They might find real pain.

SEX DYSFUNCTION AS DISEASE

Q: Would you describe sexual dysfunction as a disease?
J: A "social" disease, perhaps.
M: We would certainly have to call it a social disease in the sociologic sense. If one can presume that a neurosis is a disease, and I do so presume, then you similarly can cite it as the basis for most sexual dysfunction.
Q: If neuroses can be called diseases, then sexual dysfunctions can?
M: Yes.

Q: Because in neurosis, people also continue to function?
M: That's right. We do not consider a sexual dysfunction in the same category as an acute mental illness, let's say, schizophrenia or something like that.
Q: Would you describe it as a major problem of social health?
M: There is no question about that.

SENSATE FOCUS

Q: Would you discuss one of your major therapeutic tools, sensate focus?
M: It seems to me that what almost shouts from this section of the book is that every three-year-old is fully in touch with his own sensate focus. By the time he's six, he's begun to lose it.
J: If he's had his hands slapped a few dozen times.
M: That's right. Here's a tip for some *real* sex education: If we didn't knock sensate focus out of the kids in their formative years, we wouldn't have to reinstill it at the age of 45 in St. Louis.
J: You see, sexual response is obviously an experience of the senses which was given value by the sexual and social value systems. So if we're going to suppress these natural components by the technique of rejection in their formative stages, then certainly there will be distortion and impairment. That's why our clinic exists, to try to put Humpty Dumpty back together again. Now, we don't happen to think that social control is foreign to a natural development of sexuality. We think they go beautifully hand in hand. What is totally foreign to effective sexual development, in spite of centuries of practice, is the notion that sex is dirty, supplemented by various controls exercised through fear, rejection, ignorance and misconception. This essentially is what leads to illegitimate pregnancy. This is what engenders sexual delinquency. This attitudinal deprivation is what makes many people ill prepared to approach sexual relationships.

TOUCH THERAPY

Q: Would you explain your touch theory?
J: The touch exercises, as we introduce them, are designed to help set in motion the two major components of sexual

responsivity, physical and psychological—i.e., sexual feeling and sexual thinking. An oversimplification, of course.

M: In a very brief period of time, what we are really doing is taking the first step toward establishing communication.

J: That is very real and is deeply important to the female— that is, the ability to think and feel sexually at the same time. The young girl in this society starts correlating something that feels good with a positive attitude that affixes to another individual, but, as I've said, this usually is wrenched away; in other words, she is not told that these feelings are good and fine and that there is an appropriate time and place for them. Rather, it is implied that these feelings are unacceptable, so she starts moving her expectations, romantic concepts, and so forth, away from the feelings that ultimately are supposed to be released in marriage. So we have introduced the touch exercises in order to allow a no-demand, no-pressure, no-performance situation where she can begin to bring these feelings back together again with what they mean.

M: Touch is used to re-establish channels of communication between two people who obviously are total strangers in terms of any exchange of security and warmth and vulnerability. You've got to start somewhere, and you simply can't take two people and say, "OK, do something." You've got to give them some direction.

LOTIONS

Q: Do you relate the lotions you talk about in your book to touch?

J: Well, for some people the lotions simply enhance the touch per se, just as smooth hands and smooth bodies are an enhancement. But, in addition, the lotion is a medium of exchange. How we began to understand this is purely happenstance. It was introduced, first of all, because people coming from other climates learned that in Missouri's wintertime the skin is rough to the touch. Many began using their own products, and they just weren't working. Some produced a feeling of too much coolness; the alcohol content of others produced stinging; some were too tacky. So we turned to the professionals in the field of cosmetics and chemistry and they developed what is essentially comparable to commercially distributed moisturizing lotions. In using this product and later correlating it with our olfactory studies, which are also just beginning, we began to understand the value of this lotion as a medium of exchange. The earliest value it seemed to provide was in giving an excuse to touch each other without embarrassment. We began to realize that many who tend to reject sexual involvement are turned off by the ejaculate or the vaginal environment. So, in those cases, the lotion provided a bridge. After getting used to it in an intimate situation, people seemed to find it easier to take the next step— touching the sexual fluids. One woman's comment after touching the ejaculate was "Why, it wasn't bad at all; it was just like the lotion!"

FRAGRANCE

Q: You mentioned olfaction—the sense of smell. Your brief section on that subject was a bit inconclusive. I wondered what the implications of your studies in this area are. As with the lotions, in which you try to get people used to natural body fluids, are you also attempting the same thing with natural body odors?

J: That section of the book is inconclusive because it is inconclusive. It was a prepilot study, and we joined other researchers who wonder if odor is a part of the natural signal system of sexual attraction, desire and response. We don't know. The fragrance was added to the lotions simply as an easy way to start finding out what people think about fragrance, as a small step toward understanding olfactory preferences in a society that seems focused on removing all natural body odors and replacing them with substitutes.

Q: What do the people you interview say about body smells? Are they bothered by them or not?

J: They often say they are and turn out not to be. You see, when you remove the sense of restraint, the individual may look up in self-surprise and say, "Oh, that wasn't bad at all." And then the next time around, "Well, that was fine." So it's hard to say. You don't know whether in truth they can't stand odors or whether the aversion represents some *other* kind of dysfunction or rejection.

SEXUAL POSITIONS

Q: Something else that people tend to be uptight about are the various sexual positions. Surprisingly, you only recommend two positions in your therapy—the female-superior and the side-by-side. How come you don't drill people in the others?

M: We don't think a technical knowledge of all positions is that important, although if anyone happens to have skill at it, good for them. The reason we stress the female-superior position is that it allows a great deal of freedom in working with the distressed male. As for the side-by-side—or lateral—position, we feel it's the most effective coital position there is for both male and female, because it provides something that no other position does; that is, it does not put the responsibility on either partner to accommodate the other. Rather, it gives the chance for either or both to separately or mutually exercise whatever activity he or she desires at a given time. Nobody is pinned in this position, and it allows the greatest freedom of movement. Finally, it gives the male the greatest security of ejaculatory control.

SEXUAL IDENTITY

Q: We've had considerable discussion about sexual distress. But what would you say is sexual "health"? You use the phrase "healthy sexual identity" in your book, in fact. What do you mean by that? You also talk about "partner identification." What is that?

J: First of all, we're not employing the classic psychiatric connotation when we use "identification," which means to us, empathy, sympathy, understanding. It implies a level of communication which provides each partner with the capacity to accept the requirements of the other, understand the reasons for them, and adapt them to their mutual enhancement. As for "healthy sexual identity," whatever works for the individual would have to be so termed. Whatever works without impairing his ability to function socially or his ability to live with himself at his creative best. It follows that part of a healthy sexual identity, of course, would be that which other people can accept and reflect back to ourselves. Isn't that the way that our sense of our own identity is strengthened? If we see ourselves in a certain way, or would like to see ourselves in a certain way, it usually comes off well or not depending on how the people around us reflect their perception of it. So "healthy" would be whatever people can handle and desire to handle, and that's a very unprofessional answer.

Q: Then you don't think that for a woman, for example, her sexual identity would be eventually to have relations with a man, have children, and all the rest that conventional society expects?

J: From a sociological standpoint you're suggesting a common denominator—a commonly shared basis for female sexual identity. I would agree, but I'm not scientifically competent to say how much our identity is innate and how much acquired. As an example of the acquired, we're becoming increasingly aware that it's no longer terribly popular to have great numbers of children. So who can measure how much the reproductive drive is being allowed to remain a natural part of a modern woman's sexual identity and how much it has been put aside in favor of more socially valued expressions of female identity. Sure, I feel that a greater number of women choose to identify with conception and childbirth, just as the greater number identify themselves as women in relation to men. This I share, myself.

M: But it's certainly not an exclusive requirement. If we thought it was, we would obviously have to refuse to deal with homosexuals. And just as obviously, we don't.

COMMUNICATION

Q: Mrs. Johnson, you continue to stress the values of communication as a means of providing education. Yet there is tremendous communication today and no indication that sexual distress is decreasing. I mean, I find it hard to believe that girls who go to high school and college finally get to the altar looking and thinking like the cover photo of a 1910 issue of Saturday Evening Post. *They talk about sex. They think about it. They feel it.*

J: Well, the freedom to talk about sex is certainly increasing by the day. Any subject, from four-letter words to the specifics of copulation—as they know them—is freely exchanged in most groups of girls, boys, or mixtures of the two. But the answer to your question lies in the phrase "as they know them"—the specifics, that is. What new information, what new attitude, what new values, *other than the freedom to talk,* have been introduced? The sources of the information are the same; even the information from new sources is essentially the same. Hence, superstition and speculation, myth and fallacy have changed too little.

When I was a little girl, we used to sneak the directions on products for hygiene and anatomy out of the drugstore. I was terribly curious to know what the answers were and what they were supposed to mean to me. There was a delightful old pharmacist who knew what we were doing and he used to set things out so that we could find them. This may have been the origin of my willingness to enter research. I certainly remember how hard it was to come by meaningful answers.

All right, so the sources are more open now, but the point is, they give us little new information. The freedom to disseminate myths and misconceptions isn't going to make any appreciable change in behavior.

M: It is going to be some time, certainly another decade, before definitive information is accepted by a cross section of the population, even in view of the great increase in freedom of discussion. Our concern is that all of the old junk is still being discussed.

J: Let me, out of context, go into it a little more. The swingingest girls alive frequently report in their histories that if they don't ejaculate a male every time they are with him, they think they are failures and that he is a failure. Now, that is a fairly rigid, unrealistic imposition of one person's attitude and concept on another, especially if the particular male doesn't share the concept. That misconception is based on the notion that end-point release is the only goal, the only reason for sexual expression. It's right out of the Dark Ages, because the male should have as much opportunity as a woman to say when, what and how sexual exchange pleases him. And vice versa.

END-POINT RELEASE

Q: Would you explain in greater detail what you mean by that phrase, "end-point release"?

J: End-point release is an ultimate sexual goal—in females, it's orgasm; in males, ejaculation. But when this goal is taken as the all-encompassing, only meaningful reason to interact sexually, it doesn't serve anyone, unless they wish to conceive. That is the only reason why a goal of end-point release in the male should have to prevail. Otherwise, it should be an option, as it is for the female. In this way, it remains a natural function. Many women in this society consider men as push-button performers. They "know" that the male is a sexual being who only requires an opportunity, and if he so desires, he can perform. And that is probably the single most debilitating approach of one sex to the other. And, of course, men have an equally incorrect feeling about what constitutes a woman's requirements for sexual responsivity. It's gotten cloaked in lace and black negligees and constant repetitive reassurances of love and, in some cases, rewards; you know, I will love you if you reward me in kind.

SEXLESS MARRIAGES

Q: You've just discussed the problem of the husband or wife who demands more from the other than can be reasonably expected. Do you also run into the problem where either or both don't demand enough?

J: I think you're referring to what we have described as "reinforcing behavior patterns"—that is, patterns in which a dysfunction appears and the couple adapt their interaction to the dysfunction. You know, they tacitly agree that if they can't make it sexually, well, then they'll build up the rest of the relationship so that it will compensate for what's missing.

Q: Yes, that's it. Would you expand?

J: Let's say that two people who have little knowledge about sexual interaction marry and the sexual part of the marriage goes badly. But they have chosen one another for reasons that are important to them; they have common goals; the reasons for the marriage are well chosen, well structured. But they may share backgrounds which do not consider sex something you freely communicate about, so each partner goes about protecting the other and the relationship by defending the situation from any kind of destructive reaction. Consequently, they don't talk about it and they don't deal with it. But they go on being very kind, very thoughtful, very considerate of each other; they work at the marriage, but they walk tippy-toe around the sexual component because it hasn't worked. They are afraid it won't work again. They don't want to hurt one another or the marriage, so they do this day after week after month after year until such time as they have developed techniques of interaction that make it impossible for them to get together sexually. Yet, for religious or social or deep personal reasons, they are determined to stay together. This pattern becomes strengthened year after year. Then, suddenly, they want more from the marriage and from one another, so they ask for help. Well, then, what are we dealing with? We're dealing with real patterns of strength that have allowed them to cope with the dysfunction, and one is reluctant to take away things arbitrarily that people have found effective. We have to very carefully define the few things that are directly related to the dysfunction that make sense to the people and make sense, of course, to our psychotherapeutic concept.

M: I end up sometimes amazed at what people tolerate, how they wall the problem off, sort of like a creeping infection, and isolate it and tolerate it. "They're married," but in truth they are getting so little from the union. The most acute situation that I remember involved a married couple referred after 18 years of a marriage that had not been consummated. Now, that's a long time to sit and wait—18 years.

DYSFUNCTIONAL MARRIAGES

Q: You've made the statement that 50 percent of all marriages in this country are suffering from sexual dysfunction.
M: That's a conservative statement.
Q: Wow! I mean, that's just frightening.
J: We haven't arrived at this assumption by ourselves. It's shared by other people in the field.
M: I would also point out that this is a pure "guesstimate." No definitive sociological work has been done.
Q: By dysfunction, you mean one of the partners is not functioning.
M: Effectively. Let me give you an example that wouldn't necessarily have to do with nonorgasmic return or impotence. Suppose you have one partner with a high level of sexual demand and the other partner with a low level. This is sexual

dysfunction. Throughout the married life, if you have a major discrepancy like this, you've got a problem. Let me add that the dysfunction occurs only when two people don't understand the discrepancy and adapt to it. In other words, there are bona fide variations of level and they can change. They are not locked in. They become locked in only when people fail to communicate them and work out adaptations to them.

Q: Are you saying that virtually all of these variances in— let's call it sexual appetite—can be negotiated, that these levels can be brought together?

J: They can be negotiated to within a range of tolerance.

Q: How do you feel about the state of marriage today? Obviously, you're interested in more than sex. When a couple has problems, they come to you in order to save the marriage. I just wondered how you felt about the whole thing.

J: The fact is, we really direct our mode of psychotherapy to the marital relationship and not to the individuals involved. Obviously, the individuals are the participants in the relationship, and the history taking is devoted with very real intensity to what each individual requires and what is important to him or to her; but when we get down to actual directives, they represent the two people and their relationship. So, if you wish to say we're treating a marriage, or saving a marriage, I'd go along with that.

M: There are some interesting statistics that have developed in this regard. Certainly, the greatest cause for divorce in this country is sexual dysfunction, and any circuit judge in this country would agree with that. Of course, the sexual dysfunction can be secondary to other causes within the marital relationship.

Q: Would you agree that the sexual dysfunction is related frequently to the other problems of a marriage?

J: Oh, my, yes.

Q: Do you do counseling on the other problems, too, when you feel that they may be connected?

M: Let me put it this way. We do counseling within certain limits. We don't help the distressed couple with their bookkeeping.

Q: But you might point out that the bookkeeping is a problem?

J: Yes, that's a good way to put it.

M: Right. We may well point out that they have mother-in-law problems, but we don't tell them to drown her. The issue involved is to let them look in the mirror and see what really is distressing them and how they are frequently expressing the distress in sexual dysfunction.

J: We are addressing ourselves to the sexual component, knowing every second of the time that it cannot be separated from the rest of the marriage in any way.

M: Still addressing myself to your question, there were nine couples who came to us who had been divorced or were legally separated. They came as husband and wife. Eight of these were reconciled. One was not. Now, of the 155 couples whom we followed for five years, including this one couple who did not salvage their marriage, only four couples were divorced in five years. Now, compared to the incredible level of divorce in this country—one marriage of every three ends up in divorce court—I think that we are getting somewhere, and we firmly believe that one of the major causes for divorce is sexual dysfunction. I want to add here that I don't advocate marriage as the only thing for anybody under all circumstances. There are many people who are happily not married.

Q: Have you found that a sexual relationship can become better the longer it goes on, or can you achieve just as high a level of effectiveness with a large and changing number of partners?

J: If you are addressing yourself to the old question of sexual boredom becoming the cliché of marriage, then I would say that there is a great deal of hope developing in society that people can play the sexual game without finding it fraught with boredom. It has to do with how much quality people develop within that relationship. We gave some thought to this early in our work, which is expressed in a pair of definitions. One affixes to the term *sex,* which we use to designate specific sexual activity, varying from masturbation to intercourse and so on. The other term is *sexuality,* which we simply define as being a sexual individual, of being sexual. You are expressing this even if, by choice, you're living in a state of celibacy. You are sexual. You are a man or a woman. Your body is reacting and responding to the world around it in a sexual way, no matter how much control is imposed or how happy or unhappy you are with that control. So, if you take that dimension further, sexual expression is another dimension of personality and therefore it's another way to express yourself. It's a medium of exchange between two people. So, if a high degree of quality and attitude goes into it; if, instead of thinking of sex as a push-button thing, something you go do or something you go to have done to you; if, rather, you think of it as an expression of who you are at that time, how you feel, the time, your mood, the place and the circumstances, how can it possibly be boring?

SEX AND BIRTH CONTROL

Q: In this context, would you say that a woman who refuses to use a diaphragm has trouble accepting her body and her own sexuality?
M: Certainly, the individual who is more secure in her sexual function inevitably is less hung-up with her concerns for contraception.
J: It may not be that simple. It may be unfair to assume that just because a woman won't touch herself, she has no real sense of her own sexual identity. The fact that the little girl had her hand slapped by mamma a few times may have habituated her own touching patterns to such an extent that she really has not correlated this visceral reaction with her sense of self. Women frequently don't get around to knowing themselves very well, you know. So the touch avoidance could be just a habit, like someone who never orders lobster. A woman might not like the diaphragm for other reasons than touch.
Q: What effect do you think the pill has had on sexual performance, if any? We know what effect it has had on reproduction, but. . . .
J: Well, we know for a fact that those women who fear pregnancy welcome the security provided by the pill and develop a whole new sense of freedom to accept the sexual relationship.
M: On the other hand, there certainly are a number of women who react sexually in negative ways as far as the pill is concerned. These are women who have been on the pill for periods of time, something like 18 months up to three years,

and who noticed real loss of libido that does not return until they are removed from the pill.

Q: Is that a physiological response?

M: We have to think that it is.

J: There is a subtlety here. We say it's purely physiological, but if, as a side effect of the pill, there is a diminution of lubrication or a diminution of a sense of sexual need, desire, and so forth, then these effects can set in motion a psychological panic button that asks, "What's wrong with me?" That in turn can lead to trouble of a psychosocial kind.

CONCLUSION

Q: I was here for your press conference in May 1966, when Human Sexual Response *was published. I must say you don't seem to have the same enthusiasm now that you did then. Is the work getting you down?*

M: Well, we've had several of these press conferences in a row, and we've had major agonies in St. Louis before this. So we're tired, but still thrilled to death to be doing what we're doing. I'm 54 years old. I hope to have another ten years—even that's debatable—but I hope so. The seven-day week is debilitating and I know it. I want very much to see the original homosexual work finished. I want very much to see a top-flight training program established for the treatment of human sexual inadequacy. I want to see a really definitive research program started for *prevention* of sexual dysfunction. Above all else, I'd like to get those things done. I don't know if we can swing it, but I'm a continual optimist. So far it's worked and I continue to believe that it will. I have no idea at all where we're going to get all the money to do this, of course, but for some reason or other it keeps coming. We still run at about two thirds of what we should to be really efficient. But that's a hell of a lot better than it's been. When you move into a controversial field, you know darn well that money isn't going to flow freely. We knew that when we started. So there's no sour grapes in this at all. I certainly am not unenthusiastic, either. I think I've been very fortunate over the years to be successful in something that I thoroughly enjoy—particularly in some areas in which we've made incredible contributions. But the greatest thing that ever happened to me was coming up with a fish in my mouth such as Gini Johnson.

J: That's the first time that I've ever thought of myself in that category. Thank you.

Part 2

HUMAN
SEXUAL
RESPONSE

3

THE PLAYBOY
ADVISOR AND
MASTERS AND JOHNSON

The Playboy Advisor *is one of* PLAYBOY *magazine's most widely read features and, along with* The Playboy Forum, *reveals "everything you always wanted to know about sex"—plus a few things you didn't even think of asking. Because of these features (which, incidentally, contain a great deal of nonsexual information as well), Dr. Masters has described* PLAYBOY *as "the best available medium for sex education in America today."* PLAYBOY *returns the compliment—and maintains the high caliber of these columns—by asking Masters and Johnson to help answer questions within their field of expertise. This chapter is a collection of* Advisor *letters and answers (plus one from* The Playboy Forum) *dealing with subjects related to* Human Sexual Response, *most of which were quarterbacked by the authors of that book.*

At 39, I've been divorced for over a year and have been going with a young lady eight years my junior. Recently we broke the intimacy barrier, and we've been making love at a record-breaking clip. I feel perfectly fine, have no regrets, but am wondering about one thing. Can a man wear himself out so that in later years he'll lose his sexual adequacy?—B. B., Los Angeles, California.

The latest and most authoritative research on this subject is contained in *Human Sexual Response,* the remarkable volume by William H. Masters, M.D., and Virginia E. Johnson. This research reveals that while many men become sexually inadequate after the age of 50, this is *not* related to excessive sexual activity in earlier years; quite the contrary, the men with high performance levels in their youth tend to have similar high levels in later life.

Of even greater interest is the fact that impotence, at *any* age, is overwhelmingly psychological in origin; if he is in good health, the authors state, "little is needed to support adequacy of sexual performance in a 70- or even 80-year-old male other than some physiologic outlet or psychologic reason for a reactivated sexual interest."

Therefore, we suggest that you enjoy your sexuality, secure in the knowledge that the more you enjoy it, the more certain you can be that you will enjoy it in the future as well.

Before my wife became pregnant, she frequently experienced orgasm during intercourse. She is now in the seventh month and has not had an orgasm in all that time. We would like to know whether changes take place during pregnancy that interfere with orgasm.—F. M., Scottsdale, Arizona.

According to Masters and Johnson, many women lose interest in sex during the first three months of pregnancy, but during the second three months, the pendulum swings to a peak of sexual demand that may be higher than any prior to pregnancy. In your wife's case, the trouble may be

THE PLAYBOY ADVISOR AND THE PLAYBOY FORUM:
Originally appeared in *Playboy* magazine, August and December, 1966; February, August and September, 1967; July, August and November, 1968; April, May and November, 1969; February, March and April, 1970. Copyright © 1966, 1967, 1968, 1969 and 1970 by HMH Publishing Co. Inc. Reprinted by permission of the publisher.

that her initial decline in sexual desire caused her to worry, and this anxiety could delay her return to normal sexual response.

Aside from the psychological pros and cons, are there physiological arguments against masturbation? What is a safe, or "moderate," level of indulgence?—P. T., Stanford, California.

There are no physiological arguments against masturbation; it is as harmless as whistling. As for a "safe or moderate level of indulgence," you might be amused (and enlightened) by the following excerpt from Masters and Johnson's authoritative *Human Sexual Response*:

> Every male questioned expressed a theoretical concern for the supposed mental effects of excessive masturbation, and in every case "excessive levels" of masturbation, although not defined specifically, were considered to consist of a higher frequency than did the reported personal pattern. One man with a once-a-month masturbatory history felt once or twice a week to be excessive. . . . The [man] with the masturbatory history of two or three times a day wondered whether five or six times a day wasn't excessive and might lead to a "case of nerves."

All such fears are groundless. Whatever frequency a man has is the frequency that is natural for him. As stated in *Guide to Sexology*, "Once a month might be enough for one individual and once a day might not be too much for another . . . masturbation is self-limiting. Before 'excess,' there is simply no more erection possible."

I have been told, by a friend who should know, that when a girl becomes sexually aroused, her toes curl downward. Is this a fact or just a figment of his imagination?—R. L., Berea, Ohio.

It's a fact. Either your friend is a keen observer or he's been reading *Human Sexual Response*. Masters and Johnson have observed that muscular contractions, both voluntary and involuntary, occur throughout the body as sexual arousal grows more intense. Fingers and toes that are not being used for gripping will clench, often involuntarily. Ask your friend if he ever watched his own toes while sexually aroused; Masters and Johnson observed this phenomenon in both sexes.

Does circumcision affect the sensitivity of the head of a man's penis? I've heard that uncircumcised men are more sensitive to tactile stimulation because the heads of their penises are normally protected by foreskins. I've also heard the opposite—that the head of the circumcised penis is the more sensitive because during intercourse there is nothing to protect it from direct stimulation. Is there any truth in either of these beliefs?—G. G., Suitland, Maryland.

They're both false, according to experiments conducted by Masters and Johnson with equal numbers of circumcised and uncircumcised men:

> Routine neurologic testing for both exteroceptive and light tactile discrimination were conducted on the ventral and dorsal surfaces of the penile body, with particular attention directed toward the glans. No clinically significant difference could be established between the circumcised and the uncircumcised glans during these examinations.

This is my problem and not my husband's, I'm quite sure, because I had the same experience in relationships with several men before my marriage. I reach orgasm only when we perform the sex act with me on top. My husband generally prefers the man-above position, and in a year of marriage, I haven't had many orgasms. I have never told my husband about this, because I'm afraid he'll think there's something wrong with me. What advice can you offer?—Mrs. B. E., San Diego, California.

First, you need reassurance that there's nothing peculiar about a woman's reaching orgasm more easily in the female-superior position than in others. This has been widely reported and was recently confirmed by Masters and Johnson in *Human Sexual Response*. Several explanations are given in the sexual literature and they usually relate to the freedom of participation the woman experiences—both emotionally and physically. Most pertinent in the second area is the female's control of her movements and the opportunity for more clitoral involvement. Once you accept the fact that there's nothing wrong with you, the next step is to communicate with your husband. Tell him what pleases you and what turns you off, and learn the same information about him. Try a variety of positions, including your favorite, and, as you continue experimenting, don't stop communicating.

Until recently, my fiancée and I were both inexperienced sexually. Now, we've had intercourse several times, and each time I have been unable to control my ejaculation beyond about two minutes. She is extremely responsive, and I have been able to bring her to orgasm by means of postcoital sexplay. In addition, I have tried other recommended techniques, such as thinking about nonsexual matters during intercourse, but find that these methods tend to work only occasionally. Since we both would like her to reach climax during intercourse, is there any way I can condition myself to achieve a more normal reaction?—T. Y., Columbus, Ohio.

Your reaction is normal now—for a man to whom sexual intercourse is a new experience. To develop control over the timing of your ejaculation requires experience, regularity of intercourse and a keen interest in your partner's pleasure. The important thing is that there be real communication between you and her; both of you must feel free to talk about what you want sexually at any particular time. According to research by Masters and Johnson, before you can successfully condition yourself to delay your ejaculation, you must first learn to sense the level of sexual stimulation that immediately precedes the stage of orgasmic inevitability (just prior to ejaculation). When you've learned to identify this, ask your partner's help in remaining relatively inactive until the urge dies down; then start coital activity again. In the beginning, you may have to start and stop many times, but eventually, you should develop a sure sense of control.

There are other suggestions that can be obtained from a therapist or a physician trained in the facts now known about sexual response. However, the key factor, not only for male control but for all aspects of effective and mutually pleasurable sexual rapport, is full communication.

I have had a perfect sexual relationship with my wife for the past eight years. Recently, however, she has found herself unable to reach orgasm, even though her desire remains as strong as ever. The only variable in our sex life has been the pill, which she began taking two years ago. Do you think this could have any bearing on the problem?—B. Y., Salt Lake City, Utah.

It could. Masters and Johnson report that a small percentage of women lose their orgasmic capacity after 18 months to three years of taking oral contraceptives. As of now, it isn't known why nor how long the loss lasts. The only solution at present is to discontinue use of the pill, although you must realize that there is a greater risk of pregnancy with any other birth-control method.

After an hour or so of heavy petting, I often find myself in substantial pain in the area of my testicles and lower abdomen. I have tried, with no success, to correct this by using different types of undershorts. Can you tell me what this is, how common it is and—most importantly—what can be done about it?—O. L., Ithaca, New York.

We've been told by medical authorities that there is no scientific name for the pain you mention, but it is fairly common and is called "blueballs" in slang. Dr. William Masters said, in his *Playboy Interview* (chapter 4), "When the male is sexually excited and approaching ejaculation, the testicles increase in size; the average size increase may be as much as 50 percent over the unstimulated norm. A young male who is forced to maintain this degree of local vasocongestion for a period of time—without release—may well develop some pain and tenderness." The problem, therefore, comes not from your shorts but from your longings, and can be prevented or eliminated by ejaculation.

I have always believed that women feel the actual flow of semen at the moment of male ejaculation. My girl denies this. She claims this notion is a fantasy-wish projection, which I probably picked up from pornography. She says that in the warmth, wetness and excitement of her own sexual fervor, the spurt of fluid is simply lost to feeling. Is she unusual?— W. R., Cambridge, Massachusetts.

According to Masters and Johnson, she is not unusual, and her description is accurate.

While all the information I've seen states that masturbation is harmless for men, I've found very little in print about its effects on women. I am 20 years old and masturbate quite regularly. When I masturbate, I always have an orgasm, but this is not always true when I have intercourse. My main concern is this: Does this practice make me less responsive to my boyfriend when we make love?—Miss O. L., New Orleans, Louisiana.

Attitude is the main factor that determines the effect masturbation has on an individual. According to information provided by Masters and Johnson, masturbation, practiced without guilt to satisfy sexual needs, tends to facilitate, rather than inhibit, sexual responsiveness. When the imaginative recall or projection (fantasy) that accompanies masturbation bears sufficient resemblance to reality and conforms to the individual's personal needs and values, she'll probably find that achieving orgasm in this way will make it easier for her to respond during intercourse. Of course, if her fantasies are out of context with her experience and opportunities—violent rape, for example—and she becomes dependent on these aberrant fantasies, she may find it difficult to relate to her mate during intercourse.

Moreover, a woman's dependence on a certain technique of self-stimulation may sometimes interfere with total sexual interaction with a partner. This can be overcome if she freely communicates her desires during intercourse and if her partner and the time and place of the act are thoroughly in accord with her preferences.

You are not unusual in finding masturbation more reliable than coitus in producing orgasm. When stimulating herself, a woman can apply exactly the type of caress she prefers. In intercourse, she obviously has less immediate control; she may also have to overcome fear and guilt based on the lingering puritan ethic in our culture, as well as fear of failing to have an orgasm and thereby disappointing both herself and her partner. But intercourse can become just as reliable as a woman becomes conditioned to it and rids herself of various inhibiting anxieties.

My husband wants to broaden our sexual horizons through a variety of techniques, including anal intercourse. I don't mind most of our experiments—indeed, I enjoy them—but this proved to be very painful for me the one time we attempted it. My husband says the pain is unusual and is caused, most likely, by inhibition. He says it can't be that intrinsically painful, because male homosexuals do it all the time. Can you offer any information that will solve this problem?—Mrs. E. B., Boston, Massachusetts.

Most women find rectal mounting painful, though experience and an effective lubricant may ease the discomfort. But even women experienced in this practice generally report the technique sexually unfulfilling. An additional drawback is the possibility of infection. This risk can be lessened or eliminated if the male protects himself with a condom and protects his partner by not penetrating her vagina immediately after completing the anal act. Your husband's argument about male homosexuals and anal intercourse is irrelevant, since the practice is much less common—at least in America—than is generally supposed. As for solving your problem, you've got to weigh the importance to your husband of this variation against the strength of your personal aversion to it. Your decision will determine whether you should give it another, more extended try—counseling him to stimulate you manually at the same time—or insist that "the Greek art" is not for you.

After making love recently, during which an abundance of lubricant secreted by my girl afforded easy penetration, a second try an hour later proved impossible without the aid of a generous amount of cold cream. As this has never happened to us before, it was unnerving, especially for my girl. Can you provide an explanation, as well as some hints for preventing a recurrence?—C. D., Albuquerque, New Mexico.

Individual recovery time following coitus varies greatly among, and within, individuals, and no abnormality is necessarily indicated by your girl's lack of secretion during your second session. Neither of you should worry if the circumstances occasionally repeat themselves. But substitute a sterile lubricant, such as K-Y jelly, for the cold cream.

Please tell me if the length of time it takes for the penis to become soft after orgasm is any measure of the extent of satisfaction in the male. It seems to vary greatly.—Miss D. B., Easton, Pennsylvania.

What goes up must also come down, but nobody's figured

out a time schedule. Detumescence, a normal postejaculatory phenomenon, occurs at varying and arbitrary rates and is not a yardstick by which to reliably measure anything.

In a few months I will be marrying the greatest girl in the world, but sad to say, we are both virgins. Could you answer the following questions for us: What is the best way to enter a virgin? Do you think we should go away for a weekend before the wedding and have intercourse? Would this spare us difficulties during the honeymoon? Finally, is the size of the penis really important?—R. Z., Ludlowville, New York.

It's not the size of the wand that puts the rabbit in the hat; it's the magic of the performer. Dr. William Masters and Virginia Johnson state, in *Human Sexual Response*, A "widely accepted 'phallic fallacy' is the concept that the larger the penis, the more effective the male as a partner in coital connection." The differences in phallic sizes during erection also tend to be exaggerated. Masters and Johnson add, "The delusion that penile size is related to sexual adequacy has been founded in turn upon yet another phallic misconception. It has been presumed that full erection of the larger penis provides a significantly greater penile-size increase than does erection of the smaller penis." Actually, Masters and Johnson report, the difference in the size increase between larger flaccid and smaller flaccid sex organs is not significant.

The best way to enter a virgin is gently, after considerable sexplay. If your future wife has reason to believe that she still has her hymen, consult a gynecologist together and, after an examination, the doctor can advise you on how best to proceed with your first sexual experience.

We see no reason why you should go away for a weekend before the wedding; if you've abstained until now, you'll have plenty of opportunity after the ceremony to adjust to each other in this and other ways. The best advice we can give the both of you on your initiation into the mysteries of sex is to be understanding, tender and loving.

In a recent Playboy Advisor, *you wrote, "It's not the size of the wand that puts the rabbit in the hat; it's the magic of the performer." That is the best defense of the small penis I have ever heard, and to bolster your defense, you seek support in the Masters and Johnson book* Human Sexual Response.

In France, during World War One, an army doctor with three eager and carefully chosen assistants, including myself, started the search for an unbiased answer to the question, Is the large penis more effective than the small one? In the doctor's opinion, among the four of us we had as wide an assortment of sizes as could be found in any group. Our experiments continued from 1916 to 1925, with cooperating ladies from three continents and of at least 14 nationalities.

At the end of the first year of our work, solely with young girls, the results were inconclusive. The preferences of the subjects were divided into three almost-equal groups: Small, Large, Undecided.

It is with the mature women between 25 and 50, mothers of one to several children, that we struck pay dirt. In over seven years of work with this age group, with only an occasional examination of younger women, we found not one woman in favor of the small penis. One French lady described the small penis as an object groping in darkness in search of something to lean against.

I must add that the doctor had plans to publish our findings in some scientific paper. He was dissuaded only by fear of consequences to the thriving practice he was building up in a small eastern city.—J. P., Fort Lauderdale, Florida.

You have brought your doctor friend's "research" on penile size to light at an appropriate time—just after the publication of Professor Steven Marcus's *The Other Victorians*. Subtitled "A Study of Sexuality and Pornography in Mid–19th Century England," this book includes a perceptive analysis of how the belief in sexual myths transforms them into reality in the minds of the believers. Professor Marcus devotes the greater part of his analysis to the persistent legend that females ejaculate when they experience orgasm. Discussing a comment made by the anonymous author of *My Secret Life*, a 19th Century sexual autobiography, Marcus says:

> He believes that women ejaculate. This is one of the most widely cherished of male fantasies, and its function is self-evident. How the author acquired this belief we do not learn; but he has it as a young man, and when, at the end of his work, after he has had sexual intercourse with well over a thousand women, we learn

that he still believes it, we are justified in calling into question not only the character of his experience but the character of experience itself, seeing how deeply preconditioned it can be by our needs, by what we want it to be. For not only does he believe in female ejaculation, he also experiences it, and on countless occasions routinely describes to himself and us what it is like to experience, to feel, the seminal discharge of a woman while she is having an orgasm. There is still a further step of complication, for in addition to his—and other men's—belief, the women themselves also believed that they ejaculated, experienced this "fact," and described it to and discussed it with him.

Professor Marcus goes on to apply his analysis to your own cherished myth—that a large penis provides more pleasure to the female than a small one. Discussing a passage in *My Secret Life* in which the anonymous author expresses fear that his penis is too small, Marcus comments:

> This interest is as universal among men as their anxiety about castration, and it is not to be allayed by experience. He knows from experience that most women are quite indifferent to the size of a man's penis and that their perception of this organ is very often indistinct and imprecise (whether this common failure of perception arises from indifference or from some specific inhibition is not clear).

There are two implications in your letter, one of them being that the older women were more experienced sexually than the young girls and therefore knew more about the relation between penile size and sexual satisfaction. This is belied by Dr. Marcus's analysis, which shows that increasing experience tends to reinforce rather than diminish belief in sexual myths. Thus, in the case of the older women interviewed by your friend, their additional age and experience undoubtedly gave them more time in which to become acquainted with the fallacious folklore and more experience with which to "confirm" it.

The second implication is that the older women had larger vaginas, due to childbirth (which may be correct), and therefore needed larger penises for sexual satisfaction. This is not correct. Masters and Johnson, whose *Human Sexual Response* reflects the first truly scientific study of sex under laboratory conditions and whose conclusions we find more authoritative than your friend's "field study," point out in their section on "Vaginal Fallacies" that a large penis does not provide any more satisfaction to a woman with an enlarged vagina than does a normal or a small penis.

We think the conclusions in *Human Sexual Response* about penile size, in view of the pertinacity of the myth surrounding this subject, are also worth repeating. Masters and Johnson report that "the concept that the larger the penis, the more effective the male as a partner in coital connection" is a "phallic fallacy." They report further that the penis that appears "small" in its flaccid state grows proportionately larger during erection than the "large" flaccid penis, so that in the majority of cases, they are nearly equal in length after entering the vagina. Moreover, although the vagina expands during early excitation, Masters and Johnson report that it contracts snugly around the penis during the "plateau" phase between initial excitement and orgasm. These "involuntary accommodative reactions of the vagina" are what make intercourse gratifying, regardless of penile size.

These are the physiological facts; of course, the psychological charge a woman gets from knowing that she is being penetrated by a large penis can contribute to her sexual enjoyment—if she has been conditioned to acceptance of the myth.

Finally, if you still insist on folklore as your arbiter, we refer you to the literature of the limerick. One of our favorite five-liners explains, more pithily than any scientific tome, that while size may dazzle a lady's eyes, it takes technique to win her heart:

> There was a young man named McNamiter
> With a tool of prodigious diameter.
> But it wasn't the size
> Gave the girls a surprise,
> 'Twas his rhythm—iambic pentameter.

4

PLAYBOY INTERVIEW: MASTERS AND JOHNSON

This interview, which appeared in the May 1968 issue of
PLAYBOY, *was taped over a long weekend in St. Louis
during the middle of January. Appearing almost two years
after the publication of their first book and a little more
than two years before the publication of their next one,
the interview is the last major one in which Masters and
Johnson talked extensively about* Human Sexual Response.
*With all the controversy behind them, the scientists were
able to peer retrospectively and somewhat objectively, not
only at the facts of their work, but at much of the criticism
that had been leveled at it. Consequently, the interview,
giving some insight into the personalities of Masters and
Johnson, discussing the background to the founding of
their laboratory, stressing the basic physiological work
reported in their first book, and previewing the psychological studies of the second, provides a solid background
to an understanding of* Human Sexual Inadequacy.

It was not by chance that Dr. William H. Masters and Mrs.
Virginia E. Johnson chose staid Little, Brown & Co. to publish *Human Sexual Response.* Anxious, almost to the point
of obsession, that there be not a jot of titillation or a tittle of
prurient interest connected with their potentially sensational

book, the gynecologist and his psychologist associate sought—and found—a publishing house whose credentials for conservatism and circumspection were utterly beyond reproach. Accordingly, the proper Boston publisher covered the text in a plain brown wrapper, did not spend a penny on trade advertising and released an unprepossessing 15,000 copies to booksellers in April 1966. Little, Brown hoped only to reach a modest percentage of the estimated 250,000 American physicians for whom the book was primarily written as a text on the physiology of human sexual response.

It was with mixed feelings, therefore, that authors and publisher received the news that the initial printing was entirely sold out prior to the official publishing date. The book quickly earned a niche on *Publishers' Weekly*'s best-seller list and remained there for six months; it has sold at this writing over 300,000 copies—at ten dollars per—and continues to move at the rate of 2000 to 3000 volumes a month. Even Kinsey's best seller, *Sexual Behavior in the Human Male*, fell far short of this figure in its first year, and the average medical text sells only 10,000 copies *in toto*.

But *Human Sexual Response* is no average medical text. It contains an analysis of the most unusual experiments ever conducted in the history of science. In their St. Louis laboratory, financed originally by Washington University Medical School, Masters and Johnson observed and recorded—on color film, with conventional medical recording devices and with a unique invention of their own called an artificial phallus—the sexual response of 382 females and 312 males in the acts of intercourse and automanipulation.

The completed text, even though it contained a glossary of medical terms, may have been a disappointment to many of its nonmedical purchasers. Going out of their way not to appeal to the lay reader, the authors loaded the book with an almost impenetrable thicket of Latinate medicalese, woven into mind-boggling sentences such as "This maculopapular type of erythematous rash first appears over the epigastrium."

PLAYBOY INTERVIEW—MASTERS AND JOHNSON:
Originally appeared in the May 1968 issue of *Playboy* magazine. Copyright © 1968 by HMH Publishing Co. Inc. Reprinted by permission of the publisher.

Not even the hyperactive imagination of an Anthony Comstock could have found this prose sexually stimulating.

The rewards for those who could pierce the linguistic barrier, however, made it worth the effort. Authoritative information about the very essence of human sexuality, long a subject of emotionally charged guesswork even among scientists, was here definitively recorded for the first time. After classifying the sexual response cycle into four phases—excitement, plateau, orgasm and resolution—and describing in minute detail the physiologic and anatomic reactions accompanying these phases, the authors continued in a clinical manner to shatter long-standing myths associated with sexual response. These included the function of the clitoris, the relationship between penile size and effective sexual performance, the origin of vaginal lubrication, the nature of multiple orgasm in the female, the advisability of sex during pregnancy and among the aged.

Predictably, Masters and Johnson's research was initially subjected to sharp criticism—much of it related less to their findings than to their methods. The first salvo—fired by psychoanalyst Leslie H. Farber some time before the book was even published—set the tone for many of the subsequent attacks. In an article published in *Commentary,* Dr. Farber charged that Masters and Johnson had mechanized and dehumanized sex, that their research subjects were not typical and that they had neglected the psychological aspects of sex. "Qualities such as modesty, privacy, reticence, abstinence, chastity, fidelity, shame—could now be questioned as rather arbitrary matters that interfered with the health of the sexual parts," Farber wrote. He went on to accuse Masters and Johnson of endowing the female with orgasmic privileges that perhaps she had not earned. "My guess, which is not subject to laboratory proof," wrote Farber, "is that the female orgasm was always an occasional, though not essential, part of woman's whole sexual experience." Albert Goldman, a sociologist who wrote that the current sexual scene is dominated by "increasing homosexuality, rampant exhibitionism and voyeurism, fun-and-games rationalizations for promiscuity, masturbatory dances, sadism and other enormous proliferations of sexual fantasy," thought the text should be called *Sexual Body Mechanics* and keyed the greater part of a book review to this theme. Professor Goldman was appalled by the possibility that some of the subjects who participated in the experiments might actually have enjoyed themselves, and he was distressed by Masters and Johnson's efforts to enhance the sexuality of the elderly. "One wishes," Goldman wrote, "that we could return to the wisdom of an earlier time that accepted physical decline and sought compensation in pursuits that transcend the physical." The *Ladies' Home Journal* published an article by Lois Chevalier, who expressed grave concern that Masters and Johnson's work "ignored all the questions that it immediately raised in any ordinary person's mind—questions of morality, decency, human values."

But after the initial shock had worn off, most commentary about *Human Sexual Response* was considerably less concerned with the "decency" of the project than with its immense scientific value—specifically, with the fact that light was being shed in an area that had always been what psychoanalyst George Krupp called "the dark side of the moon." *The Journal of the American Medical Association*—long a bastion of conservatism—editorialized, "To some, sex is the ultimate area of privacy and hence not appropriate for study and evaluation. No scientific criteria can justify such a conclusion." The editorial went on to ask, "Why was this study so long in coming?" and then answered, "We may look upon Masters' investigation as a natural and inevitable consequence of changing cultural environment." Dr. Colin Hindley of the University of London commented in the *Daily Mail*, "If we are inclined to regard sexual union as something so sacrosanct that it should not be open to investigation, we should remember that a similar view was taken regarding the stars in Galileo's day."

Commenting on the specific nature of the work, *MD* magazine concluded in an editorial, "Very little of the research resembles the assumptions of some critics" and the "best measure of the study's professional acceptance . . . is that 25 medical schools have instituted courses in the physiology of human sexual response, and 14 more are beginning in the coming semester. The text in use is their book; there is no other." Medical biologist Alex Comfort predicted in the *New Statesman* that the critics of *Human Sexual Response* "will be coming round eventually for a consultation and will be glad to find that something is known about their particular problem and its management. . . . When I think of the prohibitive and moralistic kinks which have obsessed the medical men of the last two centuries, I cannot bring myself to be very anxious about Dr. Masters and his institute."

The man primarily responsible for all this tumult would seem ill cast for the role. Soft-spoken in manner, prudent in behavior, tweedy in appearance and moderate in almost all his views, William Howell Masters reminds one of the benign family physician rather than the mad scientist envisaged by some of his critics. Born in Cleveland in 1915, he was a better than average student with a strong penchant for sports, but no inkling of his medical bent until after he received his B.S. from Hamilton College at Clinton, New York, in 1938. He entered the University of Rochester School of Medicine and Dentistry in 1939 with the idea of becoming a laboratory researcher, but changed his mind under the tutelage of Dr. George Washington Corner, a famous anatomist and an unsung pioneer in the pre-Kinsey era of sex research and education. By the time he married Elisabeth Ellis in 1942 and received his M.D. degree in 1943, Masters had already set his sights on research in the physiology of sex. But he was advised by Corner to wait until he was somewhat more mature in years, until he had achieved a reputation in some research area not related to sex and until he could call upon the resources of a great university medical school to support him. (With the exception of medical-school support, these were the criteria established by Alfred Kinsey before he began his interviewing in the sociology of sex.) Accordingly, Masters trained—from 1943 to 1947—in obstetrics and gynecology and then taught these subjects at Washington University. His two children, a girl and a boy, were born in 1950 and 1951, and it was during the latter year that he was certified in his specialties. By 1954, he had published 25 papers in the medical literature and had established expertise in hormone-replacement therapy for postmenopausal women. He decided then that he was ready to begin the study of human sexual response.

He met Mary Virginia Eshelman Johnson in a highly undramatic manner—through the employment bureau of Washington University, where she had filed a job application. "I was looking for a mature woman who had a keen interest in people and who knew where babies come from," recalls Masters. "Mrs. Johnson fit all these qualifications." Born in 1925 in Springfield, Missouri, she studied music at Drury College from 1940 to 1942 and sociology at the University of Missouri from 1944 to 1947. Married in 1950, she had two children, a boy and a girl, before being divorced in 1956. Prior to joining Dr. Masters as his research associate the following year, she had had a varied background, including advertising research, administrative work and business writing. She was given a concurrent academic appointment by the Washington University School of Medicine as research assistant in 1960 and elevated to research instructor in 1962; she enrolled as a doctoral candidate in psychology at the university in 1964.

It was Mrs. Johnson who greeted PLAYBOY Assistant Managing Editor Nat Lehrman in their headquarters, the offices of the Reproductive Biology Research Foundation, which occupy a large segment of a modern medical center and resemble any doctor's chambers—except that they're more spacious and contain more physiological testing equipment. The interview began here—and ended five sessions later in Mrs. Johnson's suburban ranch home. During the entire interview, both she and Dr. Masters evinced a finely tuned anticipation of each other's thoughts, occasionally finishing each other's sentences and frequently engaging each other in animated discussion of a particular point. Mrs. Johnson, outgoing and eloquent, tended to wrap layers of illuminating qualification around hard nuggets of fact; Dr. Masters, articulate and precise, often pressed his fingertips together thoughtfully beneath his chin and peered out the window before responding to a question. We began the interview by asking them about the controversial book that turned them into unexpected celebrities.

PB: Did you anticipate censorship problems when you published Human Sexual Response?
M: No. Nor did we encounter any.
PB: Some observers think you wrote the book in dense medical language in order to spike the censors' guns. Did you have that in mind?

M: It wasn't a question of censorship as such. Medicine had not, up to that time, accepted the concept of research in this area. Kinsey's work was fundamentally sociologic, while ours dealt with the physiology, anatomy and psychology of sexual response. We were well aware that *Human Sexual Response* —which covered the first two approaches—would be evaluated in depth by the medical and behavioral professions and we wanted to avoid even a hint of titillation.

J: After working in this field for many years, we knew the emotional impact—a reaction we call the "visceral clutch"— that this research would produce, and we felt if we could soften the impact, at least until the material could be absorbed and evaluated, it would be ultimately treated more objectively.

M: Exactly. We know that in sexual matters, regardless of one's discipline or lack of it, one evaluates the material first emotionally and then intellectually—if the second evaluation ever has an opportunity to develop. If we've made the book pedantic, obtuse and difficult to read, we did it deliberately.

PB: Why did you include a glossary of medical terms in the book?

M: Because we knew that many people in a variety of non-medical disciplines would be interested—psychologists, theologians, sociologists and social workers—in fact, people in all the behavior fields.

PB: We've been told that there was a voluntary press blackout regarding your experiments while they were being conducted. Is this true?

M: Yes. We have no idea of its extent, but the St. Louis newspapers and wire services were well aware of our experiments for some years before publication of the book.

PB: Did you encourage the blackout?

M: Yes. We were gravely concerned that we would not be able to get enough work done before premature disclosure prevented an objective evaluation of the entire program.

PB: What broke the blackout?

M: A medical man wrote a highly critical article and released it to a nonmedical magazine about 18 months before the book was completed. We would have liked another year before we published the text, since we had a great deal more research to do in cardiorespiratory physiology; the book is quite weak in this section. But by that time we had been working for about ten years, and we can only say that we were extremely fortunate that the voluntary blackout lasted as long as it did. *J:* It might be pertinent to say that we have no objection now, nor did we then, to valid criticism. Unfortunately, this premature and highly personalized criticism appeared in a factual void. That is, no material relative to our research concept or design was available for comparison. We were concerned that readers of this article would therefore have no opportunity to make an objective judgment.

M: I think it important at this stage of the interview to state an integral part of our basic philosophy. We absolutely refuse to defend ourselves except in open discussion. If, for instance, a critical review of our work appears, whether it's valid or a total farce, we never write a rebuttal. We think there is only one defense, and that is continued research productivity. In anything as emotionally charged as this area, inevitably there is going to be criticism—some of real value, some useless. But if we were to spend all our time answering the critics, we wouldn't get any work done.

PB: Has there been an abundance of such criticism in the press?

M: Surprisingly little. Of approximately 700 reviews in both the medical and the lay press, some ten percent was critical; by critical, I mean the writers felt the work should not have been done for one reason or another. But 90 percent, if not totally supportive, was at least neutral; in other words, it reflected an attitude of "Let's wait and see what good can come of this research." This was a higher percentage than we dreamed of before the publication of the book. We had hoped that there would be at least half as many supportive as destructive critics. We knew darn well that if we didn't have 25-percent support, we would be in major difficulty with the medical profession. But the support was such that there has never been any question about continuing the work.

PB: What does your mail suggest about the public's attitude toward your research?

M: We've gotten thousands of letters. About eight percent of them fall into the "down with" category, of which half are vicious, obscene and unsigned. The other half of the negative letters are from fine people who simply feel that sexual behavior should not be investigated. They sign their names, they write well and we respect their opinions. Twenty-two percent of the mail has been supportive in character, and the remaining 70 percent—the part that really matters—comes from people asking for advice about their problems of sexual inadequacy.

PB: How does the crackpot mail affect each of you personally?

M: I don't think it affects me in any way.

J: Well, it's reinforcing. You always like to know that there is an applicable purpose for your work, and when you read these anonymous and scurrilous attacks, then you know that someone needs the work you're producing. As far as being personally affected—no, not really, because this mail is so obviously substandard. The only thing that really upsets me is when people like writers, scientists, physicians and others who are generally knowledgeable blithely misinterpret what we're doing.

PB: One of the greatest areas of misinterpretation relates to the purpose of the mechanical devices and equipment used in your experiments. Would you tell us about them?

M: Besides the artificial phallus, we used the routine cardiograph type of recordings for heart rate, blood pressure, pulse, respiratory rate, and so on. We also used cameras, so that we could study in slow motion what happened.

PB: In your book, you described the artificial phallus as plastic, utilizing "cold-light illumination" that allows observation and recording without distortion. You wrote, "The equipment can be adjusted for physical variations in size, weight and vaginal development. The rate and depth of penile thrust is initiated and controlled completely by the responding individual." Why did you construct this device?

M: First, let me point out that the artificial phallus was the only piece of mechanical equipment that would not be considered standard in any physiology laboratory. It was designed for intravaginal observation and photography—to show us what was happening inside the vagina during the various phases of sexual response. It was also used to evaluate intravaginal contraceptive materials. In the old days—the prepill days—the method of evaluating contraceptives was to go to a distressed area, such as Puerto Rico, and disseminate the experimental contraceptive to the population. Then the number of pregnancies was recorded, in terms of theoretical years of exposure, and a graph was plotted. We avoided any unwanted pregnancies by actually observing the action of the contraceptive in the laboratory.

There was another use for the artificial phallus that I should mention. It was used on several occasions for women or girls who were born without vaginas, a condition called "vaginal agenesis." We developed a technique in which a vagina can be created without the necessity of surgery. But the artificial phallus has long since been disassembled and we have no plans for reconstructing it.

J: This may be an appropriate time to put to rest a popular misconception created by the mass media—that is, the titillating assumption that the only purpose of the artificial phallus was to stimulate sexual response. This was not the case. During artificial coition, the research subjects never could achieve orgasm by use of the phallus alone—they all had to employ additional self-stimulation derived from their own personal preferences and previously established patterns. The point is, a female responds sexually to that which is endowed *for her* with sexual meaning. Over a period of time, all the women in our sample probably could have oriented themselves to respond to the exclusive use of a phallic device if they had been so motivated, but to them, the laboratory phallus was nothing in or of itself, and neither the situation nor their own personal interest required that they make it so. Consequently, the only reason for creating and using this device was to provide an opportunity for definition and measurement of the intravaginal environment.

PB: *In reference to your camerawork, some of your critics have maintained that you were, in effect, producing stag films.*

M: That's totally untrue. The camera was used solely to record specific physiologic reactions—skin changes, vaginal lubrication, and so on—and was directed only to one portion of the body at any time. Neither the face nor the total body was ever photographed.

PB: *Perhaps because of the abundance of mechanical equipment used in your experiments, you've frequently been criticized for "mechanizing" and "dehumanizing" sex. What's your reply?*

M: I'm not sure the equipment really has anything to do with the criticism. The heart has been measured with mechanical equipment for years, but no one accuses cardiologists of mechanization. Perhaps this concern has been raised because of an error on our part, in not clarifying the fact that we were separating two areas of focus, the physiological and the psychological. The latter will appear in a subsequent text [*Human Sexual Inadequacy*]. This was done for the purpose of clear and accurate reporting. You can't define physiologic reaction unless something happens, and this is what we were measuring. If this type of measurement is going to be called mechanization and dehumanization, then we will just have to accept it. Actually, nothing could be farther from the truth.

J: Related to this accusation of mechanization, the point has been raised that in the entire text of *Human Sexual Response,* the word *love* isn't mentioned once.

M: That's right, it isn't. But that doesn't mean we haven't been aware throughout our work that the *why* of sexual response is far more important than the *what.* We started to define the physiological facts of sexual response fundamentally because there has been such an incredible amount of misconception, fantasy and fallacy about it. Rather than present an opinion—or psychologic interpretation—we felt it was long past time in this field to find out a few basic *facts.* That's what we tried to do.

PB: Traditionalists also complain that investigations such as yours destroy the mystery of sex. Do you think that's true?

J: We happen to think that the realistic, honest aspects of sexuality are a lot more exciting than the so-called mystery. The mystery to which the traditionalists usually refer has to do with superstition and myth. A knowledge of sex doesn't impair but *enhances* it.

PB: In Human Sexual Response, *you discussed the investigative team that conducted the experiments. Of whom did it consist?*

M: The basic research team consisted of Mrs. Johnson and myself. There were others at times, but both sexes were always represented. It was obvious from the beginning that factors of comfort and security provided by the presence of both sexes made it possible for the study subjects to adapt to the research environment.

PB: Were the team members able to maintain their scientific objectivity in such an emotion-laden situation?

M: Perhaps if an individual had viewed the sex act only once in his life, he or she would have a problem, but, good heavens, we're talking about thousands and thousands of exposures!

J: In the days when the work was new, there might conceivably have been some question of getting one's own emotions under control. But we were so incredibly busy, we were so short-staffed, we were working such long hours, we were so deeply involved in trying to produce results that I don't think the problem ever occurred. I can tell you, I had no personal reaction myself.

PB: Isn't it possible that the nature of the work could cause the investigators to become sexually jaded in their private lives?

J: No more than physicians, who constantly examine people, become jaded.

PB: Is the personal relationship of the team members—or lack of it—significant in terms of their investigative effectiveness?

M: I don't think so—with this exception: Obviously, if they were bitter enemies, they would not make a very effective team. Each has to have confidence in the other's ability to handle people and to communicate effectively, because this is one of the most delicate of all social situations. The longer you work together, the more you think alike and feel alike. You start or finish each other's sentences and concepts. It's like any other endeavor involving teamwork—athletics, for instance—the best teams are the ones with the most experience at working together. But let's talk about the experimental subjects themselves, because it's they who made this thing work. I think it's terribly important to emphasize that there are a lot of courageous people who cooperated with us.

PB: How many?

M: Almost 700 by the time the book was published. Work in this field is possible only when the individual's personal value system is preserved under all circumstances. This created a situation of tremendous responsibility to protect the anonymity of all participants, which we did at all times. Secondly, we had to be sure, as much as was humanly possible, that there was no residual distress of a physiological or a psychological nature in any of our subjects, insofar as we could control it.

PB: *How did you find your subjects?*

M: In the early stages, we talked to people who we thought might be interested in this research. After knowledge of the work started spreading in the local area, we began getting a large number of volunteers.

PB: *You did some work with prostitutes, too, didn't you?*

M: Yes. But, with one exception, none of this work is reported in the book. We started with a prostitute population because we didn't know where else to start. They had a great deal to teach us and they helped in the development of recording techniques. But because we knew it would be relatively rare to find a normal pelvis in a prostitute—due to chronic pelvic blood congestion—we stopped working with them after the first 18 or 20 months and began working with the population I've described.

PB: *Did you reject many prospective subjects?*

M: About 40 percent of those who wished to join us were eliminated, either for their own protection or, in a few instances, for ours. This left us with a highly selective population, of course—a group chosen for their intelligence and for their ability to report subjectively what we were recording objectively.

PB: *Because of the selective nature of your study population, some of your critics claim that your conclusions cannot be applied to the population in general. Is this true?*

M: As it pertains to physiology, this criticism doesn't hold up, because the identical reactions were observed under all laboratory conditions. Psychologically, the criticism might be true, but we didn't make any psychological generalizations in *Human Sexual Response*. I might add, we were also selective in that we accepted only subjects who had a history of successful sexual response. If you are going to find out what happens, obviously, you must work with those to whom it happens.

J: When it came to making a choice among volunteers, we moved in the direction of those whose histories indicated stability in their past and present sexual relationships.

PB: Have you been able to assess the motivations of your volunteers?

J: When you're in a major medical center, where the use of donors and volunteers for research purposes is relatively common, the first thought concerns the money involved. We insisted on a small payment because we wanted to be able to make and keep schedules; it might seem to have been an imposition if there were no tangible return. So, especially for the younger members of the academic community, money had to be thought of as a motivation.

M: But not the only one, of course. We provided the volunteers with little more than enough money to pay for baby sitters and transportation.

J: Yes, there were other motivations as well. Almost all the subjects—even the very young ones—revealed in their interviews real concern for the state of affairs and attitudes in society today relating to sexual problems. In older people, the prevalent motivation was a reflection of some encounter with a sexually oriented distress; it could have been as commonplace as "My son and his wife are getting a divorce and we know it's because of sex." Or it could have been as dramatic as the rape of a neighbor's child, or trying to cope within the family or the community with an illegitimate pregnancy. I could give you more examples, but, to generalize, it almost always related to the thought that too little was known in the area and nobody had been doing anything about it.

PB: Don't you think any of your subjects volunteered simply to achieve socially acceptable satisfaction of sexual desire?

J: In some cases, yes. There were young women—divorcees with children, and so on—who had grave concern for their social image. They may not have had a relationship going at the time, and so the experiments served as a legitimate release for them.

PB: Were you criticized for mating unmarried subjects in the laboratory?

J: Only by the same sources who would criticize it outside the laboratory.

M: What we're really talking about is do we approve or not approve of sexual intercourse outside of marriage? All I can say is that this is an individual decision. The only unmarried subjects who were placed together in our experiments were those who had a history of similar experience in nonexperimental situations.

PB: Why did you think it necessary to study unmarried subjects?

M: As a matter of fact, we didn't think of it. The suggestion was made by a group of psychiatrists. They felt that a physical-response pattern established within marriage might not be the same as for two individuals unaccustomed to each other. When we found that there was no difference in physical response, however, we returned to marital units.

PB: In your book, you state that the subjects were recorded and observed performing "manual and mechanical manipulation, natural coition with the female partner in supine, superior or knee-chest positions and, for many female study subjects, artificial coition in supine and knee-chest positions." We've discussed the reaction of the investigative team members to their role as observers. What was the reaction of the subjects to being observed?

J: The subjects were taken through several steps of orientation before being placed in a research situation. It was a gradual process and included explanations of our motives for doing the work, of our techniques and of the laboratory environment. The individual was allowed to adapt at his own speed; some people indicated readiness faster than others. You see, it is our premise that the subjects bring their own patterns of response with them, and all we seek to do is to help preserve these patterns in a changed environment. The reassurance comes from knowing that the investigators are busy doing their particular work. There was never a situation where everyone was lined up looking. I might add, there is interrogation before each session, there is some communication during it and there is a great deal of interrogation afterward. This provides an abundance of knowledge of what the subjects think, the mood they express, the immediate-past pattern of their own life outside the laboratory. In short, we sought to eliminate any outside intrusion into the experimental situation. The subjects' own statements indicated that many times they absolutely lost a sense of the environment.

M: I think even when they didn't completely lose awareness of the investigators' presence, they learned to pay no attention to them or at least to ascribe no importance to them.

PB: In other words, the desire for privacy during the sex act was quite easily shed. Wouldn't this indicate that it's a result of cultural conditioning rather than an inherent factor?

J: Yes, there's no question that it's culturally induced. Let me mention some interesting examples related to the first part of your statement. Shy people, those who are accustomed to dressing and undressing behind closed doors, would develop enough assurance to place themselves in this environment, but they would still unconsciously preserve and observe those rituals that were important to them, even if only symbolically. They were in a situation where they had to be observed partially or totally unclothed; yet, when they were leaving a room after a sexual session, they would always reach for a robe or place a sheet around themselves. It was a token invocation of privacy, but always present and usually spontaneous. On the other hand, technicians who were only occasionally present would do their work in an unselfconscious manner, but as soon as they were finished, they would almost reflexively turn away, so that the subjects would have some private time to leave the laboratory. So we found both the investigators and the research subjects complying with this unwritten, unexpressed requirement for modesty, and even if they were only symbolic or token gestures, they were nevertheless present.

PB: Weren't you concerned that people who can perform under observation might have a response pattern different from those who require privacy?

M: If there were major variations between performing under observation and performing in private, then we would have observed them when we recorded the individual in the laboratory four or five years after his first recording. There were also multiple exposures in between, and the purported differences just did not show up. Now, we cannot state *empirically* that laboratory reaction and private reaction are identical—or, for that matter, markedly different—simply because there is no way to record a person's reactions in private. We could put an electrode in the uterus and record at a distance, but the complaint of artificiality would still be valid, because the person would know she's being recorded. We were faced with the fact that we had to move in the direction of laboratory recording or not move at all. I will say that, after thousands and thousands of recordings, we're convinced that we can translate physiological findings that we have acquired in the laboratory to the privacy of the bedroom. But I want to stress that this is just an opinion; perhaps we can never know for sure.

PB: One of your most widely publicized findings concerns the four phases of sexual response—excitement, plateau, orgasm and resolution. Quoting from your book: "The first or excitement phase of the human cycle of sexual response develops from any source of somatogenic or psychogenic stimulation. The stimulative factor is of major import in establishing sufficient increment of sexual tension to extend the cycle. . . .

"From excitement phase the human male or female enters the second or plateau phase of the sexual cycle, if effective sexual stimulation is continued. In this phase sexual tensions are intensified and subsequently reach the extreme level from which the individual ultimately may move to orgasm. . . .

"The orgasmic phase is limited to those few seconds during which the vasoconcentration [concentration of blood] and myotonia [muscle tension] developed from sexual stimuli are released. This involuntary climax is reached at any level that represents maximum sexual tension increment for the particular occasion. Subjective (sensual) awareness of orgasm is pelvic in focus, specifically concentrated in the clitoral body, vagina and uterus of the female and in the penis, prostate and seminal vesicles of the male. The human male and female resolve from the height of their orgasmic expressions into the last or resolution phase of the sexual cycle. This involuntary period of tension loss develops as a reverse reaction pattern that returns the individual through plateau and excitement levels to an unstimulated state. . . ."

You were, of course, discussing the cycle in a sexually responsive individual. But what happens to those individuals, particularly females, who don't go through the full cycle to orgasm?

M: There are periods of irritability, emotional instability, restlessness, pelvic discomfort, lack of sleep. Combinations of these symptoms may develop in the human female. You see, orgasm is a release point for the congestion of blood in the pelvis. This vasocongestion—which is the medical term for it

—is relieved very rapidly if there is orgasm. If not, the release of vasocongestion is slowed, particularly if the woman has had babies and has enlarged blood vessels in the pelvis. Her period of frustration, irritation and pelvic discomfort may last for hours, sometimes—though rarely—a day or two.

PB: *How about the male? There is a well-known malady among young men, variously referred to in slang as "blue-balls" or "lover's nuts," in which the male complains of severe pain in the testicles if he is stimulated without reaching orgasm. Is there a similar explanation for this affliction?*

M: Yes. We've discovered in our experiments that when the male is sexually excited and approaching ejaculation, the testicles increase in size; the average size increase may be as much as 50 percent over the unstimulated norm. A young male who is forced to maintain this degree of local vaso-congestion for a period of time—without release—may well develop some pain and tenderness. If he ultimately ejaculates, he never notices the local congestion, but long-standing vaso-congestion can certainly be painful. Those males who suffer from long-continued "plateau phase" frustration usually either masturbate or have a nocturnal emission, and the ejaculation relieves the congestion that way.

PB: *You used the term "ejaculation," not "orgasm." In the male, is there a distinction between the two?*

M: Male orgasm is actually a two-stage affair. The first stage is identifiable by a sensation of "ejaculatory inevitability." This is when he no longer can control the ejaculation but before he actually has any seminal-fluid emission. This stage of ejaculatory inevitability lasts two to four seconds and is occasioned by contractions of the prostate gland and possibly the seminal vesicles. This reaction pools the seminal fluid in that portion of the urethra that runs through the prostate, just outside the bladder. The remaining part of the male orgasm— that of actual ejaculation—is the expulsion of the seminal fluid throughout the length of the penile urethra by con-tractions of the penile and urethral musculature. The female orgasm, by contrast, is but a one-stage affair.

PB: *Did you discover any evidence that women ejaculate?*

M: We have heard from four women who claimed that, with orgasm, they have an overwhelming release of fluid. But we've never had the opportunity to evaluate these women in the laboratory.

J: There are large numbers of women who have physical manifestations that fit their belief that they ejaculate. The fact that many women urinate under the intensity of an emotional experience may very well be a factor here. But we don't know.

PB: You have compiled data bearing on the belief that the size of a man's penis can influence a woman's sexual responsiveness. Would you tell us about it?

M: There has long been a myth that penile size relates to male stimulative prowess. We found this not to be true. In the first place, the size of the penis usually has been judged in its flaccid state. In this situation, the penis varies greatly in size. But as it becomes erect, the smaller penis goes through much more of an erective process than does the larger penis. So, at the moment of mounting with full erection, the major differences in flaccid-penile size have been remarkably reduced. In addition, the female has the great facility of accommodating the penis, regardless of size, and not expanding the vagina beyond the size sufficient for containment. Vaginal expansion, of course, is purely involuntary and is directed toward accommodation of the particular penis in its erect state.

J: It helps to realize that the vagina is a potential rather than an actual space in its unstimulated state. Actually, the vagina is virtually an infinitely expandable organ. After all, it goes from a collapsed state to a size large enough to accommodate a baby's head.

M: Of course, we have been talking about physiological response. Psychologically, if the woman really believes that the larger penis in its flaccid state is going to make a difference when it becomes erect, then for her it might. But the really experienced woman would agree that size doesn't make a crucial difference. There are physical exceptions concerning obstetrical trauma that should be mentioned. Vaginal tears or alterations can result in a chronically distended organ that might have difficulty adjusting to the erect penis, *regardless* of its size.

PB: Another penile myth concerns the sexual responsiveness of the circumcised versus the uncircumcised penis. What can you tell us about this?

M: The uncircumcised male—and, in some versions of the folklore, the *circumcised* male—is presumed to have a greater tendency toward premature ejaculation, because he can be more easily stimulated. We have no evidence that either presumption is true. Fundamentally, we can't find any differences in reaction time, or sensate focus, between the circumcised and the uncircumcised male.

PB: Yet another misconception discussed in your book relates to the controversial Freudian theory about the clitoral versus the vaginal orgasm. Would you elaborate?

M: It was Freud's concept that if a woman's response was restricted to the masturbatory, or clitoral, orgasm, then it reflected psychic immaturity. She could be considered a fully responsive, hence mature, woman only if she had orgasm during intercourse—by definition, the vaginal orgasm. In order to delineate between these two types of orgasm, Freud presumed they were entirely separate physiological entities. Our research indicates that this is not the case. Certain clitoral changes occur with stimulation of either the clitoral area or the vaginal area, or from manipulation of the breasts or, for that matter, from simple fantasy. These changes are anatomically and physiologically *identical,* regardless of the source of stimulation. Secondarily, it is physically impossible *not* to stimulate the clitoris during intercourse. And I'm not referring to direct penile-clitoral contact.

PB: Didn't Freud speculate that the sexually mature woman has transferred sexual sensation from the clitoris to the vagina?

M: Yes, but there is no longer any need to speculate about this, because, as I started to say, the clitoris *is* stimulated during intercourse every time the female responds to a male thrust. This reaction occurs regardless of what position she may be in. You see, with each thrust, the minor labia are pulled down toward the rectum and, in the process, stimulate the shaft of the clitoris. So there is no physiological difference among clitoral orgasm, vaginal orgasm, breast orgasm or, for that matter, orgasm through fantasy. Incidentally, since the publication of the text, we've had the opportunity to evaluate three women who can fantasy to orgasm.

PB: Manual stimulation of the clitoris by the male—as a form of foreplay—is strongly recommended in most marriage manuals. Does your research confirm the wisdom of this advice?
M: Not entirely. Many marriage manuals err in suggesting that the glans of the clitoris be manipulated; this is an extremely tender area, which the female rarely manipulates herself. She more or less stimulates herself along the shaft or just in the general clitoral area, which is called the *mons*.
PB: What about "riding high"—another favored marriage-manual concept—in which the male maneuvers his body so that the shaft of the penis comes into direct contact with the clitoris?
M: This is a misconception. Our findings show that the clitoris elevates and withdraws from its overhang position during intercourse, making it extremely difficult to attain direct penile shaft–clitoral contact. It can be done, but it's an acrobatic maneuver in most cases and not really worth the effort.
PB: Did your research shed any light on the folkloric connection between female orgasm and conception?
M: We have no sure knowledge of this. We certainly have some notion that an occasional and probably very rare female may ovulate more than once in a menstrual cycle, notably as the result of very effective sexual response. But this material has never been released, because we don't have enough information to support it scientifically. All we can say is that we are strongly suspicious. On the other side of the coin, there is reasonable evidence to suggest that, in some instances, a sexual inadequacy—a lack of effective response pattern for the female—may be part and parcel of a psychogenically induced infertility.
PB: Some of your critics think that your work contributes to a general overemphasis of the subject of female orgasm. What's your reply?
M: We don't think you can overemphasize the importance of this subject. But it certainly has been belabored out of its proper context. The Sixties could be labeled the decade of orgasmic preoccupation. It's been only in the past seven or eight years that this focus on female orgasm has emerged. Some women are developing a fear of nonperformance as a result of all the public discussion about its importance—

particularly discussion not necessarily based on scientific objectivity. You can't read any women's magazine today without finding an article about some form of reproductive biology. It may sell magazines, but it also creates a scare type of philosophy that, in turn, may increase either male or female fears of inadequacy.

J: Orgasmic preoccupation could occur only in a society in which sexuality has been so negated that many women have been unable to move confidently through all this discussion with a foundation of self-knowledge. A woman who has or has had a satisfactory relationship—and is secure in its effectiveness—can skim through the magazine article stressing orgasm or listen to the neighbor lady at the coffee klatch brag, "Oh, we have intercourse eight times a week and I'm orgasmic one hundred percent of the time," and still not feel threatened by this kind of discussion. But someone who lacks personal knowledge can be thrown into pure panic.

PB: In your book, you also discussed female multiple orgasm. You wrote, "Women have the response potential of returning to another orgasmic experience from any point in the resolution phase if they submit to the reapplication of effective stimulation." Since multiple orgasm was discussed by Kinsey and earlier by L. M. Terman, what particular significance did you attach to it?

M: Apart from several physiologic observations of a technical nature, one of the important things we established—to our own satisfaction, at least—is that the female is *naturally* multiorgasmic. This had not been emphasized before.

J: In spite of Terman and Kinsey, scientifically oriented people still imply that this is a freakish thing.

PB: Picking up on the phrase "naturally multiorgasmic," do you believe that, all other things being equal, the female should achieve orgasm as easily as the male?

M: Yes, indeed. We have nothing to suggest otherwise. It would seem that puritan and Victorian social restraints have destroyed or altered significantly the female's natural responsivity.

PB: Another aspect of female sexuality discussed in your text is the notion that the female's sexual response is more diffuse than the male's—that is, that women respond sexually with

more of their bodies than do men, whose pleasure seems to be centered in the penis. Would you comment on that?
J: This, too, is probably culturally conditioned. We find that those men who value total expression undergo all the thrill and sensate experience of a total-body phenomenon commonly attributed only to the female.

M: I think what should be stressed here is that physiologically, the male and the female are incredibly *alike* in sexual response —not different. This is really what we tried to emphasize in the text.

J: If I may be permitted to comment on the larger issue implicit in your question—the fact that so many people of *both* sexes feel sexual pleasure only in the sex organs themselves—this is a manifestation of their rejection of their total sexuality. For example, a lot of women do not respond to breast stimulation because of its implied impropriety. A young person exposed to this type of negation will frequently reject the concept of breast stimulation and/or response. An anesthesia comparable with self-hypnosis is induced. I mention the breasts particularly because this type of negation comes out so dramatically when women reject nursing.

M: Yes, and this negation may extend even to the genitals— as with the unresponsive woman who claims she never feels a thing during intercourse, no stimulation whatsoever. She has a certain amount of vaginal anesthesia that we're convinced— as are many others—is psychogenically induced and relates to attitude, circumstance and environment. I do want to stress, however, that we lack definitive data concerning the psychological deterrents to sexual response and sexual tension.

PB: *You use the phrase "sexual tension" frequently in your book. Would you define it?*
M: Sexual tension is the physiological concomitant to, and reflection of, elevation in an individual's psychic sex interest, expressed in increased blood concentration and muscle tension.

J: If that seems formidable, try to think of it as what the body does in response to sexual interest.

PB: *Does this tension differ in any way from what is usually referred to as the sex drive?*
J: Sex drive has become such a general term that it doesn't have a precise scientific meaning. It's often used to mean the basic drive to reproduce.

PB: Can sexual tension be suppressed or denied?

J: It can be denied and it can be displaced—that is, expressed in a nonsexual way. Most likely, if suppressed, it will be expressed involuntarily, through nocturnal emissions and erections or pelvic vasocongestion and vaginal lubrication. These cannot be put aside.

PB: Do women experience anything analogous to the male nocturnal emission?

M: We have done no dream research, but we're certain that the female can be orgasmic in dreams.

J: And there have been frequent reports of an increase in the volume of erotic dreaming by women who have been abstaining from sex.

M: Returning to your question about sexual denial, I'd like to add that sexual demand seems to be a unique physiological entity. Unlike other demands, it can be withdrawn from; it can be delayed or postponed indefinitely. You can't do this with bowel function or cardiac or respiratory function. Perhaps because it can be influenced in this unique manner, sex has been pulled out of context. Lawyers and legislators have taken a hand in telling us how to regulate sexual activity. They don't, of course, presume to regulate heart rate, but, as I say, sexual demand can be denied, even on a lifetime basis.

PB: With no ill effects?

M: That depends. We've already talked about irritability and pelvic discomfort that can result from not fulfilling sexual demand, but these effects are only temporary. On a long-term basis, many different types of neurosis can develop from continued suppression of sexual tension. But not always; there must be countless lifetime celibates who have not become neurotic.

PB: It is common for women to abstain from sex during menstruation. Are their sex-tension levels lower then?

M: Not necessarily. A woman can certainly be responsive during her menstrual period—particularly the terminal part—if she is effectively stimulated. Only a small percentage of women, however, report their *greatest* level of sexual tension during menstruation.

J: Physiologically, the explanation lies in the vasocongestive factor we discussed earlier. Obviously, the blood concentration in the pelvis increases during menstruation, especially in women who have had babies. This is translatable as sexual sensation. If a woman psychologically rejects the concept of sex during menstruation, she may successfully put her sexual feelings aside. Then, too, there are women who feel great discomfort during their periods, which can blunt sexual desire. On the other hand, if the psychosocial circumstance is overwhelming—such as being reunited with a partner—then this can be an overriding influence in favor of sexual desire.

PB: Many sexologists have speculated that women have a recurring cycle of sexual desire, most commonly believed to occur the week before menstruation. Did your research confirm this?

M: If you're speaking of a physiological constant that's true for all women, the answer is no. Many women can identify a higher level of sexual tension the week or so before they menstruate. Fewer identify their highest level as the week after menstruation. An even smaller percentage are those who feel their highest tension during the ovulatory period. The smallest percentage, as I've said, are those whose desire is highest during menstruation. Probably the greatest number of women report *no* constantly identifiable pattern of response.

J: There are so many factors that make this difficult to pin down. For some women, sexual deprivation sends their need and interest up. On the other hand, we find that frequency of exposure with a high frequency of orgasmic return helps maintain a high level of sexual stimulation—in other words, success breeds success.

PB: What role do such psychological factors as fantasy and imagination play in enhancing sexual response for either sex?

J: It depends on how you define those terms. What some people call imagination could be described as recall. The only psychological constant in sexual response is the memory of, or the conditioned response to, the pleasure of sensation—in other words, to those things that have become sexually endowed for that person. These may be deliberately invoked during masturbation or during intercourse to help overcome a particular environment or occasion—a time or a place that doesn't turn the individual on.

M: Imagination, as we define it, plays a very real part in sexual response, but it varies tremendously with individuals.

Usually, it is employed during the excitement or early-plateau phases, but at the moment of orgasmic expression, the individual usually is immersed in his own sensate focus.

J: I do want to emphasize that imagination, as we understand it, relates not to fantasy but to reality, to a recall or use of the realities of a person's life. True fantasy—in other words, the invention of thought patterns related to sex or sexuality—is generally employed by those individuals who have had little or no previous successful experience.

PB: Obviously, imagination would have great value with a sex partner who was not physically attractive. Have you found that physical attractiveness is important to successful sex response?

J: Again, all these things are terribly individual. In this society, there are certain stereotypes of attractiveness, but even these have variations. If an individual reminds you of someone else who has brought pleasure, or connotes warmth or other valued attributes, that person is perceived as attractive and thereby sexually stimulating apart from the stereotype. We can't make a general statement—except to repeat the perceptive cliché that beauty is in the eye of the beholder.

PB: In your experience as investigators, however, aren't there certain aspects of appearance that seem more stimulating than others for many American men—characteristics such as breast size, for example?

M: If you talk about breast size, you have to mention Madison Avenue and PLAYBOY, because they have created connotations of sexuality in connection with it. As a matter of fact, the larger-breasted female may not be more responsive.

J: Worse yet, a woman's preoccupation with her symbolic sex quality might cancel out her attention to, or her involvement with, her real sexuality. I think that would be the most common pitfall. On the other hand, her symbolic sexual qualities might make her conceive of herself as more of a sexual person; consequently, she might involve herself with more enthusiasm. I'm not an anthropologist, but I think there is evidence that the attraction of the female breast relates to the mother-figure concept.

M: And yet, in the male population, there are hip watchers, leg watchers. It varies.

PB: Do you have any idea how these individual predilections develop?

M: Personal conditioning, I would guess. Maybe the first exposure to sexuality was a woman with particularly attractive legs or breasts.

PB: In your experience, are women aroused by the sight of male nudity?

M: Kinsey felt that the female was essentially unaroused by the unclothed male, but this has not been the case in our experience.

J: We have come through an era in which the male body was considered quite unbeautiful. Men wore tops at the beaches, and so on. Many women built in a rejection. They weren't supposed to look, but sometimes they did and liked what they saw; so their private and public behavior were quite different. Given equal opportunity, women will react to sexual anatomy just as men do—just as much or just as little, if society permits them to and if they begin to think of themselves as sexual beings.

PB: Would you make the same generalization about pornography—that it has equal erotic potential for women and for men?

M: According to our experience, yes. The greatest variations relate to an individual's background and personal preference, rather than to his or her sex.

PB: Do you think pornography would continue to have its arousing effects if it were made more easily available and lost its taboo quality?

J: Our attitude, like everyone else's, is purely speculative. But we think pornography certainly gains in its excitement by being forbidden.

PB: Do you think it advisable to control its availability?

J: I think the only control necessary is in the formation of attitudes by the individual throughout his or her life. As far as censorship is concerned, I don't think there's any real contribution to the goodness of an individual's life in telling him what he can or cannot read or see.

M: What is a matter of indifference to one individual may be repugnant to a second and incredibly erotic to a third. This is one of the reasons the legal profession has never been able to establish a satisfactory definition of pornography.

J: And they never will, because that which is forbidden is changing all the time. As far as I'm concerned, it's a matter of taste.

PB: Many people become sexually aroused by stimuli less obvious than the human body or graphic portrayals and descriptions of it. Can you tell us anything about these indirect erotic stimuli?

J: We think nonspecific erotica—as we call it—is an expression of the fact that we are total sexual beings; we are male and we are female, and we have many reminders of this that are not just sociocultural or psychosocial. Each sex wears certain clothing—though this is up for grabs now—and there are certain signals that remind us of the fact that we are sexual beings. To answer your question more directly, a nonspecifically erotic stimulus is something that gives visual, tactile or other sensory pleasure. It isn't pelvically oriented. It could be a hand that evokes a memory and a sensation. It could be a fragrance, a color, a movement, a musical strain—any stimuli of the senses. But it has to be translated through the individual's unique experience in order for it to have sexual connotations. Being nonspecific, it might be meaningless to someone else.

PB: We've been discussing your research; valuable as it appears to be, some of your critics maintain that it is academic, that it doesn't really teach people how to improve their sex lives. Do you have some practical or clinical application in mind for your findings?

M: In order to talk about that, I'll have to explain the total concept of our Reproductive Biology Research Foundation: There are three major areas of interest—all related to reproductive biology—and each has a laboratory and a clinical purpose. In 1947, research began in conceptive physiology; shortly thereafter, the clinical application of this work was developed by treating married couples who had difficulty in conceiving and/or maintaining their pregnancies. In 1952, our work in contraceptive physiology was originated, with obvious clinical application to population control.

The year 1954 marked the beginning of our research in human sexual physiology. The clinical application began in 1959 as a long-range program for the treatment of human sexual inadequacy. By this we mean such basic complaints as frigidity, impotence and premature ejaculation. We can talk to you only in general terms about this material, because we feel that the specifics should not be released until we have ten years of statistical follow-up. Our tenth year is 1968, and by the end of this year, our basic formal research design will have been completed. The findings will be incorporated in a medical text called *Human Sexual Inadequacy*, which is scheduled for publication in 1970. This text will deal not only with the concepts of treatment of sexual inadequacy developed during these years but also with the psychology of sexual response as developed, described and evaluated in the original research population for *Human Sexual Response*. We are greatly encouraged by the results of the clinical programs and by the long-range statistical evaluation of these results. There is a great deal of hope in the future for people who suffer from those sexual inadequacies I mentioned. These individuals can have every real confidence that there is a good chance for a reversal of their symptoms.

J: We never lose sight of the fact that the underlying commitment of this research is to replace fallacy with fact, with the hope that less sexual distress will occur in an enlightened society.

PB: Taking these inadequacies in the order in which you mentioned them, let's talk about frigidity. Do you mean it simply to describe the condition of a nonorgasmic female?

M: Frigidity means many things to different people. It *can* mean a nonorgasmic female. Many a husband has sent his wife to a physician with the complaint that she is frigid, when actually she is orgasmic only once a week and he is interested in a high level of response two or three times a week. Sometimes the word *orgasm* doesn't enter into it at all. It may be simply that a woman just doesn't have much interest in sex. Frigidity means one thing to a Freudian analyst and has entirely different meanings to other concerned parties.

PB: What are the basic causes of female failure to have orgasm?

J: Primarily, they're attitudinal. But failure to achieve orgasm is attitudinal for thousands of different reasons, so it's really impossible to generalize.

PB: Is there such a thing as a physiologically unresponsive woman?

M: Maybe two or three percent of nonorgasmic women have enough basic pathology in the pelvis to account for pain during coital activity. As a result of the pain, these few may not be totally responsive. But lack of response is, in more than 90 percent of the cases, psychogenic rather than physiological.

PB: Do you go along with the psychiatric notion that nymphomania is really a manifestation of frigidity?

J: We think that *nymphomania* is a much abused term. There are many manifestations of sexual tension that could be described by this word. Take, for instance, the woman who is psychologically satisfied with the sexual activity in her life; she does not feel deprived. Yet this particular woman subsequently may have experienced one or more pregnancies or other conditions that increase the pelvic blood supply. This causes a condition that often produces a genital sensation identical to the sensation produced by sexual stimulation. Because she has experienced sexual response, the woman identifies this feeling as being sexual, even though sexual need is not on her mind at all, but she has a physical reminder that can be translated into sexual need. You could call this nymphomania. The same condition could develop for a woman who stands on her feet for hours. She may notice the same sensation and translate it within her experience as sexual stimulation. She may not feel emotionally in need of sexual activity; she may not really be deprived in any way, but the physical feeling is there. For some women this is an annoyance, but for others it may become a signal to seek an increase in their frequency of sexual outlet. This, too, could be called nymphomania.

As for the specific question you raised, I suppose there is a category of woman who stays at high plateau and rarely or never achieves orgasm but develops and sustains a level of sensation so intense as to produce a desire for an unusual frequency of sexual activity. This situation resembles the psychiatric definition of nymphomania.

M: If you want our favorite definition, we agree with Wardell Pomeroy—one of the coauthors of the Kinsey reports—that a nymphomaniac is a woman who has just a bit more sex tension than her partner.

J: Exactly. The concept of nymphomania is purely relative. Response comes to mean more to one woman than it does to another and either more or less to the same woman at different times.

M: Many of the misconceptions about nymphomania stem from the lack of understanding that the female can be multiorgasmic.

PB: What about prostitutes? In your experience, are they generally as frigid as is widely believed?

M: The notion that as a group they are frigid is a misconception. In our in-depth interrogations of prostitutes, we found that the second-greatest motivation for moving into or continuing in prostitution was sexual desire. The first motivation, of course, was economic.

PB: The second sexual inadequacy you mentioned as part of your long-range research program is impotence. What is your definition of the term?

M: Like frigidity, impotence is defined in many ways. We classify it as two types. In primary impotence, the male has failed at his first opportunity at penetration and continues to fail at every exposure thereafter to achieve and/or to maintain an erection for the length of time sufficient to accomplish mounting. In secondary impotence, the male has not failed his first time or his first thousand times, but then begins to develop difficulties in achieving or maintaining an erection.

PB: What is the chief cause of impotence?

M: Fear. Regardless of why or under what circumstances the male fails to achieve or maintain an erection the first time, the greatest cause of continual sexual dysfunction thereafter is his fear of nonperformance. Those who have had an instance of failure due, let's say, to fatigue or excessive alcohol intake and do not attach special significance to it rarely develop this fear. But those who elevate an occasional failure out of context and dwell on it retrospectively can go on to develop severe cases of secondary impotence.

J: Alcohol is probably a great cause of secondary impotence.

M: Shakespeare showed great psychological insight when he had the porter in *Macbeth* tell MacDuff that alcohol "provokes the desire but it takes away the performance." It disinhibits the desire to perform, but it inhibits those physical reactions that lead to successful performance.

J: If the male realizes that a failure because of alcohol—or any number of other factors, such as untoward circumstances, the wrong person, the wrong place, or what have you—is not meaningful in terms of his masculinity, that it is not a signal for continued incapacity, then he can be home free.

PB: Is it possible, as some critics have suggested, that the female's sexual emancipation—and the consequent increase in her sexual demands on the male—is a significant cause of impotence?

M: Any situation conceived as threatening by a particular male may tend to make him fearful about his performance and thereby lead him to try forcing the situation. But one doesn't need female emancipation to do this.

PB: The final sexual inadequacy you mentioned is premature ejaculation. Is this as difficult to define as the others?

M: Well, I've never heard a satisfactory definition—and that includes our own. But as a working definition, we describe a premature ejaculator as a male who can't control the ejaculatory process long enough to satisfy his partner at least 50 percent of the time. Obviously, such a definition does not hold up if the partner happens to be nonorgasmic. As for the causes, they vary. I suppose one of the greatest causes in a 40-year-old male is exposure to prostitutes in his late teens and early 20s, with its pressure for speed and performance and lack of regard for time, place and circumstances. There's also the back-seat-of-a-car type of exposure, in which a quick-response pattern develops when the young man is just learning. In all these situations, there is rarely any concern for the female's satisfaction.

PB: Many men try to overcome their problem of premature ejaculation or that of orgasmic failure on the part of their partners by developing a self-conscious sexual technique. Assiduously memorizing sexual lore and following the suggestions of many marriage manuals, they recite the multiplication tables silently during intercourse, or think of the stock market, in order to postpone ejaculation. Doesn't this preoccupation with technique defeat its intended purpose?

J: Of course. It shouldn't be necessary to recite multiplication tables in order to withhold ejaculation. It's the quality of the sexual encounter, the attitudes that one brings to it regarding the *desire* for control that are important.

M: Fundamentally, the greatest mistake the male can make is to feel that because he has a certain amount of technical competence, he is therefore an effective sexual entity. Technical competence, as sexual information becomes more available, will almost be *presumed.* It's the male's approach, his concept, his expression, his giving of himself, the personal relationships he establishes that get the job done for him *and* for her.

PB: Many marriage manuals rhapsodize about the simultaneous orgasm—which a great number of couples find difficult to achieve. Is this another aspect of the self-consciousness we're discussing?

J: Yes, it's an intrusion on the spontaneity that is the secret of sexual response. It's a lovely thing when it happens. It certainly produces a greater sense of sharing, which should heighten the experience. But to deliberately try for it would be an imposition of technique.

PB: You also mentioned research by your foundation in conception and contraception. Have you made any revolutionary discoveries in solving the problems of infertility?

M: I don't know how revolutionary our discoveries are, but we have learned that a knowledge of when to have intercourse, how to have intercourse and how often to have intercourse could solve one out of every eight infertility problems in this country. In 20 years of evaluating infertile marriages, we have found that at least 60 percent of the difficulty, when the problem is unilateral, has been on the male side. It makes one think about the queens in history who were beheaded because they produced no heir to the throne.

And just one final point about fertility that would be apt for PLAYBOY's large male audience. It is a common fallacy that frequency of performance is likely to induce pregnancy. But the fact is that it takes the average fertile male 30 to 40 hours after an ejaculation to return the sperm production and seminal-fluid volume to his normal range. If a male happens to have a low sperm count, it may take him as long as 48 hours. So if his performance during his wife's fertile period is too frequent, she is less likely to become pregnant, because his sperm count will never get the opportunity to reconstitute itself.

PB: In your studies, have you reached any conclusions about the relative effectiveness of contraceptives?

M: Yes, but our conclusions don't differ substantially from what is already known. Far and away, the most effective contraceptive aid is the pill; second, in terms of statistical security from pregnancy, is the intra-uterine device—the I. U. D., or coil. In our experience, the chemical intravaginal contraceptives, together with recently developed foams and creams, are next in line, followed very closely by the diaphragm/jelly routine and the condom. The suppository and foam tablet are not as adequate as these other contraceptives.

J: They don't cover the right places at the right times.

PB: Do any of these birth-control devices affect sexual response?

M: Some women reject the intravaginal chemical contraceptives on an aesthetic basis, and that might interfere with sexual responsivity. In some women, the pills create a feeling of nausea; this detracts from the users' sense of well-being and, in turn, may blunt sexual response. The intra-uterine device sometimes causes cramping and bleeding. All of these factors are relevant. On the other side, some males find that condoms interfere with erective adequacy during intercourse. This is rare, but it happens.

J: And a few men are irritated by chemical contraceptives. We've had very few reports about this, but the reports we have seem quite authentic.

M: We can't discuss this subject in further detail, because our research isn't yet complete. And much of what we have discovered about conception and contraception hasn't been released yet to the medical press. There's an old medical saw —with which I happen to agree—that says, "Doctors don't like to read their medicine in *The Reader's Digest.*"

PB: Apparently there has been very little definitive sexual information circulated among physicians. For example, we noted that you devoted several paragraphs of your text to an explanation that masturbation doesn't cause insanity. Did you really think it necessary to stress this obvious fact in a book written for doctors?

M: Yes—simply because many times we have been asked that particular question by members of the medical profession at professional meetings. This isn't surprising when you consider that, with a few exceptions, medical courses in the basic area of sexual response were not initiated until as recently as 1964. Physicians who graduated from medical school before that time had no opportunity to be oriented specifically to the subject. Since 1964, it is my understanding that somewhere between 40 and 50 medical schools—out of a possible 92— have begun teaching courses in sexual response. This represents a real revolution in medical education.

PB: What are the significant areas of sexual ignorance among medical students and physicians?

M: They know no more and no less about the subject than other college graduates. They share most of the common misconceptions, taboos and fallacies of their nonmedical confreres.

PB: A common medical taboo—which has recently come under fire in sex-education circles—concerns the prohibition of sex during certain stages of pregnancy. Some doctors forbid intercourse for as long as three months before and three months after birth. Did your research confirm the wisdom of this prohibition?

M: Most doctors we know of don't go this far in their prohibition of sexual activity—although in our interrogations we did hear of some. We found no reason for such long-continued abstinence, particularly during the last trimester of pregnancy—providing the female partner has no pain and providing the membranes aren't ruptured and that there is no postcoital bleeding. We firmly believe that there is no real reason not to continue sexual activity up to the very terminal stages of pregnancy. After childbirth, of course, the situation varies tremendously. Usually, any prohibition of a month to six weeks is reasonable because of the trauma to the vaginal canal occasioned by the delivery and/or the episiotomy— the surgical incision of the vulvar orifice—that accompanies childbirth.

PB: Another area of medical uncertainty and misconception relates to sex among the aged. What can you tell us about your research on this subject?

M: There are two fundamental constants necessary for the

human male and female to maintain effective sexual function into the 80-year age group: One, the individual must be in a reasonably good state of general health; and, two, he or she must have an interested partner.

For the female, an effective sexual function in her earlier years encourages continued successful functioning as she ages, primarily because she isn't contending with fears of nonperformance. If the female has not been particularly effective before menopause, then the added concerns of the aging process may make her totally ineffective thereafter. But if she has been responsive and well oriented sexually, she usually sails through the menopausal situation with no significant variation in her sexual-response pattern.

As for the male, if he has had satisfactorily active sexual experience during his teens, 20s, 30s and 40s, there's no reason he can't maintain sexual effectiveness into his 50s, 60s and 70s, if he meets the criteria already described.

J: The only thing I'd like to add is that aging may cause some reduction in the urge to ejaculate—that is, in the need for *frequency* of ejaculation. But, contrary to popular belief, this has nothing to do with the older man's ability to achieve and maintain an erection.

PB: Is any progress being made in training physicians to assume a responsible role as sex counselors?

M: The concerns of sexual behavior have probably received more attention in the medical profession than has any other topic in the past five years. The profession is making a massive effort at self-education and is to be congratulated for it.

PB: How about sex education for laymen? At what age do you believe it should begin?

M: It should begin as soon as youngsters are old enough to observe their parents relating to each other.

PB: What can you teach children about sex at such an early age?

M: I don't think you have to "teach" them anything. If there is real warmth and interpersonal exchange in the marital relationship, the kids absorb it.

PB: Do you think sex education should be restricted to the home?

M: No. It should be taught in the church and in the school as well. I don't think you can teach it any one place and do it well. Most homes can't teach reproductive biology—apart from unsophisticated "where babies come from" answers. At the other extreme, some homes teach all the biology in the world, but the kids never see mom and dad holding hands. The point is that parents can and should demonstrate to children the importance of an effective and outgoing sexual relationship.

J: There's a kind of pseudo-avant-garde parent who wants so much to be "in" that he or she will overtalk the subject of sex. There will be great freedom with terminology and a studied, self-conscious atmosphere will be created, but no values will be imparted.

M: Religious authorities should present their views, of course; and as for the schools, sex education should be a part of the curriculum, but I don't have any definitive opinions about how that should be done.

J: One of the problems that hasn't been solved as yet is who should do the teaching. A good teacher of sex education has to impart some of his personality. He has to teach that sexuality is good and that there is a place for it. He has to teach values that are realistic, that make sense in the context of how things really are. It seems sad to me that we feel it necessary to design sex-education "curricula" and put formidable barriers around the subject. We have not yet learned how to treat the subject naturally.

PB: A. S. Neill makes a similar point in Summerhill—*that once we are faced with a concept of sex education, we have already failed at it. In other words, sexuality should be learned naturally, from life experience.*

M: Yes, but, of course, Neill was dealing with a controlled environment in his progressive school. As American society is constituted today, we have to make the best of a sorry bargain, which means some sex education on a formal basis, at least for the foreseeable future.

J: You know, there is a kind of natural sex education in the communication of children with one another.

M: The kids spread a lot of fallacies and misconceptions, but they have one thing going for them: They learn to talk about sex. Even if it's hush-hush or snicker-snicker, there's value in communication.

J: The pitfall in this is that knowledge picked up from the peer group frequently works as a barrier to sex education from adults. Often a good job can't really be done at home because one has to contend with misinformation conveyed by other people's children, not to mention teachers who insist on making judgments.

PB: *What qualifications do you think are desirable for teachers of sex education?*

M: A sense of confidence and a nonjudgmental approach to the concerns of sexual response. A certain amount of academic orientation is in order, but all the academic orientation in the world won't amount to a row of beans if the teacher isn't comfortable with the subject.

J: Besides being well informed, he or she should have *lived* the subject—in other words, should have had the experience of a stabilized sexual relationship.

PB: *When you say that teachers should be nonjudgmental, do you mean in terms of teaching when it's right and when it's wrong to engage in sex?*

M: No, we don't mean that. Everyone has a right to teach his own basic concepts, but sexual activity must be taught as a perfectly natural, normal phenomenon of human expression and not one that should be hidden, avoided or discussed in whispers.

J: If you're really going to guide and direct young people, you have to be willing to listen to and accept their experiences as they express them in a classroom situation. If you express any condemnation there, you can turn off a young person, as far as communicating his or her sexual experiences is concerned, and thereby lose a vital opportunity to provide guidance.

PB: *Do you think sex education should include contraceptive information?*

M: Depending on the age group, certainly. To my mind, the greatest tragedy in the dissemination of contraceptive information is that it's usually disseminated after the young person has started having intercourse. Rarely is there pregnancy protection at the first opportunity.

PB: *What do you think of Wilhelm Reich's claim that society's taboos on infant, child and adolescent sexuality are responsible for impotence and frigidity in adults?*

M: I think in some instances he is quite correct. This is a contributing cause in many of the cases we have seen.

J: And the effect of these taboos is frequently a factor that has had to be *overcome* even by those who don't develop problems because of them.

PB: Do you think masturbation plays an important role in an adolescent's sexual development?

M: That depends on the individual. There is a large number of people who have never masturbated and yet have developed into sexually responsive adults. So you can't say it's a requirement. But, obviously, it has played a major role in the sexual development of most individuals.

J: I wonder if the negative side isn't more important. The fact of masturbation is nowhere near as dramatic a concern as the misconception that it's dirty, objectionable or what have you. Of course, this starts the individual out with a concept of guilt. A permissiveness about early genital expression is not nearly so important as the *absence* of a negative approach.

PB: On the whole, how well do you think sex education is being handled in America today?

M: We have no scientific knowledge as to whether it's worth a damn. There are a lot of people who climb on the sex-education band wagon and say it's great. But somebody is going to have to take the time and effort to find out whether there is any real value in the entire concept of formally disseminating sexual information to youngsters. I don't mean to say that I think sex education is valueless; I just want to emphasize that there is absolutely no objective study that has been done in this area to determine its real value.

J: Yes, but the fact that sex education is being done at all has greater value--at least at this point--than the actual material being disseminated. Wouldn't you agree?

M: Of course. The mere fact that one can talk about the subject and consider it with some degree of objectivity—all this shows incredible progress.

PB: The kind of progress you're talking about is part of what's been called the Sexual Revolution—a revolution that is defined in many ways by many people. Can you give us your own definition?

J: To begin with, we don't call it a revolution; we call it a renaissance. People tend to forget that the greatest deterrent to female freedom of sexual expression in this country was the invention of the steamboat—in other words, the Industrial Revolution.

M: It was this that pulled the men off the farms and into the city. In an agricultural community, female sexual equality never became an issue. Time and time again, mom—in order to avoid the kids—would take pop's lunch out into the back field. They had lunch—and something more—by the creek under a shade tree. Fulfillment was thus taken for granted. Sex in this culture was presumed, valued, enjoyed—and lived. Then, as we became an industrial culture, puritanism spread and eventually Victorianism took over. With it came the repression of female sexuality that has existed until very recent years—the "thou shalt nots," the double standard, and so on.

J: So you see, we're talking about a *rebirth* of natural sexuality. We're beginning to hark back to a time when there was an earthy acceptance of oneself as a sexual being, when sex was taken for granted as a healthy part of life. If I may inject a personal note, our work is very much a reflection of this renaissance. Even though people have been somewhat shaken by it, society has still *permitted* it.

M: Precisely. We have not existed in spite of our time; we have existed *because* of it.

J: Actually, Kinsey was a pioneer—and so were R. L. Dickenson and Havelock Ellis before him. But they reflected a deep cultural need. We have emerged as a reflection of society's changing attitudes. For example, Bill started as a gynecologist—a physician—and I know that his early interest in the basic science of sex research developed almost parallel with the maturation of society's attitudes toward the subject. Kinsey, on the other hand, pioneered this renaissance; he helped lead it and make it what it is.

PB: Many critics of this sexual renaissance, as you know, think that the pendulum has swung too far in the direction of permissiveness, that the new emphasis on sex has inflated its importance out of proper proportion.

M: If the importance of sex was ever overemphasized—by its obsessive and moralistic negation—it was in the Victorian period, not now. It was then, not now, that sex could not be accepted and that sexuality was denied as a dimension of the total personality. If the pendulum has swung too far, I'm sure it will swing back. Let's put it this way: A certain amount of healthy objectivity needs to be injected into the field. We hope that something like this interview—appearing in the magazine I regard as the best available medium for sex education in America today—will help do it.

PB: You are obviously pleased to see the double standard disappear. But many clergymen fear that the vanishing "thou shalt nots" are being replaced by libertarian "thou shalts" that may deprive young women, by virtue of a kind of reverse puritanism, of their freedom of choice. Do you see this happening?

M: Absolutely not. What has developed with the use of contraception is a new sense of selectivity for young women. They now have more freedom to say no than they ever had before. It may have something to do with the fact that the female no longer makes her decisions on the basis of fear— fear of pregnancy, fear of disease, fear of social ostracism. In no sense does this imply a rejection of elective chastity, but chastity based on the innumerable fears is entirely a false premise; an objective decision cannot be made on this basis. Today the young woman is free to make her choice, pick her time, her place, her circumstance, without the old fears. With all the druthers now available to her, we have a hunch that the intelligent girl tends to be more sophisticated in her selection—simply because it is *her* selection.

J: If effective contraception is being used, then a woman must be honest with herself and realize that she is engaging in sexual activity as an expression of herself within a relationship. She is not, consciously or unconsciously, playing the old game of sex for marriage entrapment, nor is she using sex to represent her femaleness by "willful exposure to unwanted pregnancy"—to quote Dr. Hans Lehfeldt's tongue-in-cheek but accurate comment.

PB: Do you think it's possible, as some clergymen predict, that the elimination of fear will break down all the barriers?

M: Is it possible? Yes. But there is no reason to believe that removal of fear inevitably results in the destruction of value systems. In fact, there is some evidence that modern young men and women are much more concerned with the quality of interpersonal relationships than with sex per se.

I: What I'm about to say may not go over well with some PLAYBOY readers, but the fact is that for the first time in many decades, the girl is running the sexual show. She is not a victim; she doesn't have to put up or shut up. Although this issue is still in limbo, we're on the right road toward placing value on sexual activity within a human relationship as opposed to simple emphasis on natural drives—you know, 'Let's do it, even though the timing is wrong, the people are wrong and the place is wrong; we have to satisfy a natural human need." The young woman now has many things to contemplate in making her choice. She can decide, after proper self-evaluation, whether her goal is reproduction and homemaking or whether she wants to express herself in some other fashion while deferring—or even rejecting—marriage. There are so many options to consider, and the concerns of venereal disease, pregnancy or social ostracism need no longer be the foremost factors in influencing her decision.

PB: *Then you don't think that the pill culture necessarily leads to promiscuity.*

M: It depends on what you mean by promiscuity.

PB: *What do you mean by it?*

I: In our concept of the term, someone who exploits another person sexually is promiscuous, regardless of the circumstances.

M: Sexual expression to me is either mutual orientation, satisfaction, enhancement and stimulation or it's promiscuous —inside or outside marriage. The old concept of sexual promiscuity, meaning excessive interest outside of socially approved channels, leaves me cold. A woman who adequately serves three different men sexually and enjoys all of them, and gives each as good as she gets, is more honest than the "faithful" wife in her own bedroom who serves one man but thinks of another. I think there is both mental and physical promiscuity—the latter being the old concept. The more dishonest concept, and the one that offers the least hope of effective development of mature sexuality, is mental promiscuity. Let me give you another example. Take the young male who makes seven chalk marks on the wall in one night. As far as I'm concerned, he may be promiscuous—mentally rather than physically—if he is interested in his partner only as a proving ground for his sexual athleticism.

PB: There have been predictions that another by-product of increasing sexual freedom will be the proliferation of homosexuality. What do you think?

M: If the majority of reasons given by scientists and by homosexuals themselves for turning to homosexuality are true, a liberalization of sexual attitudes would remove some of these reasons; it would help lessen the homosexual's self-rejection. This is, of course, only theorizing. We have no evidence to support it.

PB: Marshall McLuhan predicts that the gradual blurring of stereotyped psychosexual roles for men and women will soon make the differences between the sexes less significant than the similarities. Add to this the influence of the pill, he says, and it will become "possible for sexual woman to act like sexual man." Do you think we're heading toward a kind of unisexual society?

J: Unisex is a rather unappealing term, but McLuhan is obviously correct in predicting that the old stereotypes of male and female will disappear; to an extent, they already have. We no longer require a stronger sex to go out and kill the tigers and to defend the home. Most of us know that the football hero and the physically well-endowed woman are not necessarily more effective sexually than the rest of us. So why don't we turn to the important things—like real communication and re-enforcement of one another's reason for being? Why concentrate on wearing ruffles to prove we're women and unadorned clothing to prove we're men? It hardly seems important to have a program to tell the players apart; the players know very well who they are—or if they don't, clothing will hardly solve the problem.

PB: One more prediction related to the sexual renaissance is that it will weaken and perhaps even obsolesce the institution of marriage. What are your views?

J: Society has not yet come up with any social grouping more functional than marriage and the family. Quite obviously, we think the renaissance of sexuality will strengthen it, not weaken it.

PB: How so?

J: One of the most threatening things to the marital relationship is the separation of sex and sexuality—sex being the physical expression of sexual activity and sexuality being a dimension or expression of the total personality. The Victorians negated sexuality and thereby made sex a behind-the-stairs, in-the-dark sort of thing. Communication regarding sexual matters most likely did not exist. There may have been people who worked this out in the privacy of their own one-to-one relationship, but all the evidence tells us that this was the exception, not the rule. The point is that sexuality can hardly flourish in a forbidden atmosphere. If two people enter into a sexual relationship, they have to let it live on a 24-hour basis. Sexual response can be sparked by the fact of its being forbidden, just as it can be triggered by hostility—but that's hardly a lovely way to live and it certainly doesn't create an aura of love, of affection, of warmth to be conveyed to children. So I think that marriage has endured in *spite* of the Victorian attitudes, not because of them. I should add that, in my opinion, marriage is not a static institution; in the future, it may be constituted differently. It's undergoing change today, but I don't think it will be altered in a noticeable way during our lifetime.

PB: What can you tell us about the future of sex research—specifically, your own?

M: At the moment, we're working on the biochemistry of reproductive fluids—that is, such things as vaginal lubrication, Bartholin's and Cowper's glands secretions. No work has ever been done in these areas. We're also doing a great deal of work in homosexuality and have been since early 1963. We're studying the female homosexual in particular, as we feel she has never been examined in depth. We want to learn as much as we can from the sociological, physiological, biochemical, endocrinological—and, ultimately, the therapeutic —points of view. But any concept of therapy is far beyond our current concern and we won't have anything to report for perhaps a decade or more. At the moment we're merely learning about the subject.

PB: What is your goal in the homosexual research?

M: We hope eventually to move into some concept of sexual reversal for those who wish it. From what we know now—which is very little—we can't conceive of homosexuality of itself as an inversion or abnormality. It seems to be a basic form of sexual expression—a minority form but a very definitive one.

We also want to continue working in sexual physiology, but hopefully we're well past the nose-counting stage of experimentation reflected in *Human Sexual Response*. Our future projects in this area are quite specific and include investigation of sexual response as it relates to the damaged heart—that is, the coronary, the hypertensive and rheumatic hearts. We're also particularly interested in studying the sexuality of the aging population, in terms of understanding metabolic, endocrinological and physiological changes involved, with the ultimate goal of enhancing the effectiveness of sexual response among the aged. And we certainly hope to do some work on the massive problem related to the sexuality of the physically handicapped.

PB: What do you think the future holds for sex research in general?

M: Sufficient maturity and controlled expansion, we hope, so that research may be done in the *total* area of sexual behavior —not just from the psychological and physiological points of view, the "why" and the "what," but also, for example, from the sociological and theological perspectives.

Human sexual behavior is of vital concern to every single individual throughout his or her life. Aside from the instinct for self-preservation, it is the most forceful response we know. Yet it is the response about which we know least. Look at the massive amount of time and effort that has been spent on the control of poliomyelitis, for instance—an effort that was worthy, since it brought the disease under control—but compare the occasional individual who contracts polio with the daily concern of *every* individual about his or her sexuality. Although we are obviously in favor of any medical approach that helps eliminate the major pathologies, it must also be realized that the one physiological activity, after eating and sleeping, that occupies the greatest part of human life is no less worthy of definitive and objective research. We intend to devote the greatest part of *our* lives to that research.

Part 3

THE
PSYCHOTHERAPEUTIC
BACKGROUND

5

PSYCHOANALYTIC UNDERSTANDING AND TREATMENT OF IMPOTENCE

Homer C. Curtis, M.D.

Some of the bitterest hostility directed at Masters and Johnson has come from members of the psychiatric profession. Their serious criticism, in a nutshell, is that rapid therapies tend to treat symptoms rather than delve into the unconscious for causes, some of which may be buried way back in childhood experiences. So, the reasoning goes, if you remove a symptom (such as impotence) without treating the cause (let's say, a conflict arising from a distorted parental relationship), then the unresolved conflict may erupt in the guise of new symptoms other than the one removed. Thus, the basic problem remains in spite of the alleged cure. Masters and Johnson do not deny this possibility, but they point out that a debilitating sexual distress is more than just a symptom; it can itself be the cause of even greater conflicts than the underlying one. Moreover, they freely concur that patients whose problems require more than two weeks of psychotherapy should certainly begin or continue with other, longer-range therapies, in addition to the foundation's rapid treatment. In short, they don't in all cases recommend their own therapy as a substitute, merely as a supplement.

The next two chapters are written by psychiatrists who represent the traditional psychoanalytic views about im-

potence and frigidity, but who are not hostile to the Masters and Johnson system. An understanding of what Drs. Curtis and Moore have to say is doubly useful, for it demonstrates the type of thinking—virtually the only type that existed until recently—that Masters and Johnson have used as a point of departure (and in many cases departed from). But it also demonstrates on the part of both psychiatrists an effort to bridge the gap between the older and newer therapies. They do this by examining what common elements do exist and by furthering an exchange of information between the therapies.

Dr. Homer Curtis is on the psychiatric staff of Hahnemann Hospital in Philadelphia.

Much has been written in the past several years concerning the possible effect of the Masters and Johnson research on psychoanalytic theory. Some authors have felt that these findings would force important revisions in analytic thinking in matters such as bisexuality and female sexuality. It has been my impression that perhaps the majority of psychoanalysts have been very much interested in this work and have welcomed the additional biological information to confirm or to modify psychoanalytic theory, which has been evolving steadily for nearly 80 years. In fact, the readiness of analysts to applaud the Masters and Johnson work is related in part to recent developments in analytic thinking that from a psychological point of view anticipate the conclusions derived from physiological research.

Those psychoanalytic ideas that the Masters and Johnson data seem to controvert are abstract concepts several steps removed from clinical theory that is based solidly on clinical observation. These concepts were attempts by Freud to fill in gaps that psychoanalytic methodology could not fill. The psychoanalytic method of data gathering is essentially psychological introspection and empathy. It cannot be expected

PSYCHOANALYTIC UNDERSTANDING AND TREATMENT OF IMPOTENCE: From *Sexual Function and Dysfunction*, edited by Paul Jay Fink, M.D., and Van Buren O. Hammett, M.D. Copyright © 1969 by F. A. Davis Company. Reprinted by permission of the author, editors and publisher.

to provide data available only through other social or physical methodologies. Freud, therefore, drew on the then-available concepts of biology, anthropology and anatomy and expected that advances in these other sciences would replace or supplement some of his theoretical constructs. Psychoanalysis cannot provide data regarding the way the genitals develop physically or how they function physiologically. However, it can determine how sexual development and function are experienced psychologically and their effect on psychic growth and function.

In the border areas between various disciplines, disagreement and conflict can occur, but with objectivity and communication we can expect mutually beneficial results. For example, Masters and Johnson have helped connect physiology and psychic responses, and psychoanalysts can avoid approaches to patients that might be influenced by nonphysiologic theorizing. In return, we may be able to help Masters and Johnson understand some of the meaning of their therapeutic-counseling techniques that are based on an intuitive understanding of the intrapsychic and interpersonal problems interfering with normal sexual functioning.

From another point of view, it is not surprising that psychoanalysts are sympathetic toward Masters and Johnson's work. The history of the development of psychoanalysis can attest that research into the secrets of sex has always encountered much resistance. Freud's pioneering efforts to subject the problems of sexuality to scientific scrutiny have contributed to the relatively more favorable climate in which Dr. Masters and Mrs. Johnson have been working. However, I am sure that they can testify that the battle to abolish the irrational taboos on knowing about sex is not yet won.

Although it is appropriate to compare Masters and Johnson's work and its reception with that accorded Freud, there is an important difference in the degree of resistance. The difference in degree is due to a qualitative factor—namely, the resistance to accepting the primitive, unconscious meanings of sexuality. Research into the physiology of sex encounters, of course, some of the same opposition attached to breaking the taboo of looking at and knowing about the sex organs. In the face of realistic physical evidence and measurements, the resistance can retreat to a position where the physical facts are accepted but the psychological facts are still ignored or accepted in an attenuated form. This retreat has already been demonstrated. Some of the initial doubts and resistance to this research have diminished, and some people have rushed to embrace this work and to use it as part of an effort to deny important aspects of the psychological meanings of sex. By elevating the physiology of sex to a place of exclusive interest, such people justify their need to avoid awareness of the primitive sexual misconceptions and conflicts of childhood that have persisted into adult life, which have always been and will continue to be the basic cause of sexual problems.

It is gratifying to know that Masters and Johnson do not fall into this trap. In their writings and lectures they demonstrate the basic importance of the emotional factors. Even when advocating certain physical measures in the treatment of sexual problems, they state that this therapy is only part of a program of building up confidence and open communication between partners rather than the answer in itself.

For the sake of convenience, we can divide psychological impotence into various forms on the basis of the manifest type of disturbance of sexual function. Although these different dysfunctions usually are related to specific underlying psychic problems, careful investigation also reveals wide similarities. For this reason, I would include premature ejaculation, retarded ejaculation and relative lack of pleasure with orgasm under the heading of impotence, in addition to the difficulties in achieving or maintaining erection. This general classification is supported by clinical experience with men who show many or all of these dysfunctions at different times.

For example, one patient, who at first denied having a sexual problem, stated that his lack of any heterosexual experience was simply a matter of not finding any girl he was ready to marry. As the result of analysis, he could see that he was actually rationalizing an avoidance of women because of anxiety. He then felt able to permit himself to form closer relations with a woman but found himself unable to get an erection even with prolonged sexual stimulation. With continued therapy, he could attain erection but always found a reason to avoid intercourse by saying that he felt too tired or feared discovery. The patient next advanced to having erection and ejaculation while fully clothed and pressing against the girl. After several more days he could bring himself to attempt intercourse, only to have premature ejaculation before entry. He then encountered great difficulty in insertion and needed the girl's help in overcoming this barrier. Even after accomplishing insertion, he expressed the feeling that his penis didn't seem to fit properly.

As he overcame this problem, he next complained even after successful insertion that he experienced no pleasure, only a sense of deadness, and that he was unable to ejaculate. He soon became aware of some pleasure with intercourse but for some time could not reach ejaculation. Although he finally achieved ejaculation, he needed the help of perverse fantasies that had usually accompanied masturbation. The experience left him without much orgastic pleasure, and he described the experience as a feeling of seepage or flowing out, like urination. After considerably more analytic work, he could have pleasurable orgasm but felt unable to claim credit for it, attributing this success to my help. In fact, he told his girlfriend that she was working on one end and I on the other, as if he could not take credit or responsibility himself.

This refusal to accept responsibility was later replaced by a gamelike attitude, as if to say, "This is a silly game, not to be taken seriously." In this connection, the patient recalled a childhood game of crossing his fingers to deny that he meant what he was saying or doing. This game epitomized his approach to any activity where he had to commit himself. Eventually, he reached a point where he wanted to marry the girl, but he was troubled by a sense of uneasiness and was aware that he was looking for reasons to delay what he felt was a dangerous, all-out commitment. He also worried that he might have a heart attack due to the exertion of intercourse and frequently had diarrhea after ejaculation.

This instructive series of sexual difficulties occurred over a period of about six months and gave the impression of the sexual conflict fighting a desperate rear-guard action to continue its hold on the patient who progressively strengthened his mature control over his sexual function. At one time or another, he exhibited all the usual types of male sexual dysfunction, all in the service of avoiding what seemed to him to be a dangerous assertion of masculinity.

In addition to illustrating the variability in type of physiologic dysfunction, this case demonstrates a frequent and more basic psychological factor. When this patient achieved a reasonably good physiologic performance, he would resort to ideas, attitudes or actions that served the purpose of denying or minimizing what he was doing. In addition to the "keeping the fingers crossed" kind of game, anything that provides emotional or physical distance may permit some degree of potency by neutralizing the danger of closeness and commitment. The physical position may have special meaning, as it does when a man is potent only when having intercourse from the rear, as if to avoid seeing the woman's face. A related phenomenon is the ability to have intercourse only with women who are considered bad or degraded, while being impotent with a "good" woman. Variations of this malady are common and appear even in literature, as in Goldsmith's *She Stoops to Conquer*. In the treatment of such patients, it is found that the "good" woman who is loved and respected must be kept asexual and pure inasmuch as she represents the tabooed, pure mother of childhood. The "bad" woman is sufficiently remote from the image of mother to be used as a degraded object.

Another example of this tendency occurred in a man with occasional erective impotence; after starting to have intercourse with his wife with feelings of love and warmth, he suddenly lost his erection. At this point, a fantasy spontaneously came to mind. He pictured himself as an awkward adolescent trying to have intercourse with an older woman who was laughing at his efforts. To his surprise, his erection returned, and with the help of the fantasy he was able to complete the act, although without much pleasure. In analyzing this experience, he realized that to feel too much love for his wife made him anxious and that he felt forced to retreat into impotence. However, he seemed able to strike a bargain, to settle for the lesser evil of being weak, humiliated, and impotent in his fantasy, in order to regain his physical potency with his wife. It was, of course, a cramped, restricted potency, inasmuch as it meant an emotional withdrawal from the woman he loved.

The problem of premature ejaculation is relatively common and offers more difficulty in diagnosis and understanding than does erective impotence. As Kinsey points out, in many men of lower socioeconomic levels, it is taken as a matter of fact that ejaculation should be reached as quickly as possible, and the female's response is not taken into consideration. From this observation and from comparison with other mammals where quick ejaculation is the rule, Kinsey concludes that rapid ejaculation is not only normal but perhaps even biologically superior. Fortunately for his argument, he neglects to consider those cases where ejaculation always occurs before intromission, leading to a fertility problem that could hardly be considered biologically superior. He also does not endear himself to his feminine readers when he labels the rapidly ejaculating male superior, "however inconvenient and unfortunate his qualities may be from the standpoint of the wife in the relationship."

This conclusion is typical of Kinsey's restricted view of human function and behavior, a view in which he leaves out the important dimensions of subjective experience and the interpersonal effect of sexual functioning. In comparing man with the chimpanzee that ejaculates in 10 to 20 seconds, Kinsey ignores the biologically based evolutionary gains that provide man with a potential capacity for consideration of the needs and welfare of his partner to a far greater extent than other mammals. That man also has a capacity to control his ejaculation within certain limits is clear from the experience of most men as they gain sexual and emotional maturity. These two capacities seem to go hand in hand as we study normal maturation and even more dramatically as we observe recovery achieved in our patients with premature ejaculation. This connection between ejaculatory control and mature emotional relations with women is not an absolute one. In my experience, the patients who have persistent premature ejaculation always demonstrate important psychopathology in their relationships with women, as evidenced by their retention of a childish view of women as dangerous, dirty and degraded.

Certainly, not all rapid ejaculation is due to fixed psychopathology. There is no doubt that there is a factor of learning and experience in the control of ejaculation. There are variations in the speed of ejaculation not only between individuals, but also in the same individual on different occasions. Such elements as degree of excitement or time elapsed since the previous ejaculation can be operative. However, more important is the psychic state, where anxiety and hostility can exert decisive influence. The normal male who has demonstrated his ability to control his ejaculation to provide maximum pleasure for himself and his wife in a relaxed, loving atmosphere may temporarily lose that control when anger or anxiety intrudes. An example would be the experience of a man whose wife for reasons of her own seemed to lose interest and made a comment about a household problem during intercourse. This remark annoyed the husband, who promptly ejaculated and experienced the orgasm as distinctly less pleasurable than usual.

It is impossible, of course, to use some specific time standard as normal. Here the overt behavior does not lend itself to understanding the quality of sexual function. The decisive issue is the underlying meaning and motivation, such as lack of experience on the one hand or specific intrapsychic conflict on the other. That the latter is a frequent cause in many cases is readily determined in those male patients who come to psychiatric treatment with a chief complaint of premature ejaculation. Not only is this often a gross disturbance, such as ejaculation consistently prior to intromission, but often the patient recognizes that even if he succeeds in entering the vagina, he has little or no control. He often will describe the sensation as a flowing out like urine, with weak orgastic contractions and relatively little pleasure. There is usually an available standard of comparison the patient applies, not only from masturbation but also from successful experiences of longer-lasting, more pleasurable coitus with his wife or with other women. A striking example of this occurred in one man who could make intercourse last as long as he pleased if he knew that his partner of the moment was unable to have orgasm but would inevitably ejaculate prematurely if he had reason to believe the partner could have, and expected him to give her, an orgasm.

Obviously it is unwise to extrapolate from clinical experience with patients and assume that comparable overt dysfunction has the same significance in all cases. Above all, we must recognize that there are multiple forces determining behavior and function and that the final common pathway or compromise will depend on the relative strengths of the various forces. Thus, we could say that we all have some sexual anxiety left over from our childhood misconceptions and fantasies, but its influence will depend on how much is present, how it is handled by the psychic defenses and how much is available in the way of adaptive resources such as sublimation.

A further factor in the over-all picture of integrated mind-body functioning is the choice of symptom or method of expression of any existing psychopathology. Serious psychopathology may affect only certain functions, leaving others relatively unimpaired. This fact is demonstrated in the selection of premature ejaculation with the sparing of erective potency, for example, or with the formation of neurotic symptoms such as phobias or obsessions, with retention of a relatively good physiologic sexual function. I stress the words *relatively* and *physiologic,* inasmuch as we usually find evidence of some disturbance of sexual function in people with fixed psychopathology, if only in the way in which the patient experiences the psychological relationship with his sexual partner.

It would be appropriate at this point to sketch out a general picture of the psychological factors usually discovered in psychoanalytic investigation of men with sexual dysfunction of a fixed nature. One broad differentiation can be made on the basis of the degree to which the psychopathology has extended beyond the symptomatic interference with sexual physiology and has pervaded the character of the patient. As a matter of fact, we usually find that a patient with impotence will also have some qualities of character that express in a nonsexual way the same meaning underlying the impotence. For example, some impotent men may show a social anxiety and hesitance that reflect the same fear of injury or sense of shame on which the impotence is based. They may have severe restrictions in their capacity to feel warmth and sympathy with other people. It is true that the very fact of suffering from impotence may have secondary effects on a man's social behavior and interest in others, but careful scrutiny of the patient's history and development usually reveals that the traits in question existed from childhood on, before the beginning of active heterosexual functioning. It is usually found that extensive characterological effects of psychopathology mean a less favorable prognosis.

A composite picture built up from a study of a number of men with persistent sexual dysfunction would include such traits as social conformity, overpoliteness, introversion and difficulty in self-assertion. They are apt to be more concerned with intellectual achievement than social or athletic interests. In their attitude toward women, they are usually shy, anxious, passive and dependent; or in reaction against these characteristics, they may develop Don Juanism, with shallow, short-lived relationships. In their dealings with men, they tend to avoid open clashes, may compete intellectually rather than physically, and are apt to be deferential. Once again, these attitudes may be covered by an overcompensatory rivalry with men.

Beneath the descriptive behavioral level, these patients often conceive of women as lusty amazons who dominate men and demand satisfaction. They do not feel they are men among men and look at other men with envy and feelings of incompetence. There is a disturbance of masculine identification, and passive, feminine tendencies may find expression or be covered up by repetitive attempts to prove virility.

Typically, the childhood background revealed in such patients includes a mother described as pampering, smothering, guilt-promoting and sexually provocative toward the son. The fathers are either apathetic, rejecting or absent on one hand, or brutal and punitive on the other. In either case, there is no real attachment between the father and son. The proximity of the mother and the distance of the father exaggerates the natural sexual urges and resulting anxieties that flourish in every child. These anxieties subside naturally as maturation and favorable experiences with loving, yet reasonable parents correct the childish misconceptions of his relationships with his parents. A loving, warm father who at the same time is strong and firm helps the boy neutralize his unrealistic fantasies and fears, and the boy then can make a strong masculine identification with his father. In the absence of such a father, these fantasies run wild until buried by repression, inhibition and character restriction. Instead of coming to resolution, this conflict remains dynamically active, even though unconscious, and exerts its influence indirectly through symptoms such as impotence and related character distortions.

Having sketched the picture of the severe clinical case of impotence, we need the perspective afforded by a view of the milder, temporary variations of sexual dysfunctions. Most normally potent men have at some time experienced some form of impotence. The cause of a transient episode may be obvious, as in situations where the man is fearful of discovery, or it may be impossible to find any reason. In most cases, however, it is possible to trace it to some emotional reaction to the partner or the situation, which temporarily interferes with sexual function. In other cases, some acute problem in the man's personal life has demanded his attention, making it difficult for him to sustain any sexual interest.

In these cases of temporary sexual failure, the major emphasis may rightly be placed on some current external or conscious problem. However, careful inquiry will usually reveal clues of additional predisposing factors or specific susceptibility to some external problem. For example, one man may be impotent where there is some danger of discovery, whereas another might find this a challenge and a stimulus. Or fatigue and preoccupation with business may lead to failure with one man, whereas another with the same worries seems especially eager and able, as if sexual intercourse is a refuge and solace.

These few examples make us aware that even in an apparently simple, transitory episode of impotence there are apt to be complicated interacting factors representing different segments of the man's psychic make-up. Some of these factors will be conscious, realistic reactions; others will be unconscious, irrational and primitive. Any human behavior partakes of a number of motivations and psychological reactions, which combine in a final common pathway of verbal or motor expression. As an example of this, consider the case of a man who, at a party celebrating his wedding anniversary, felt that another man, an admired single friend, was too attentive to his wife, who did not appear sufficiently insulted by these attentions. The husband was annoyed and angry with his wife, yet would have felt guilty to spoil the special occasion by verbalizing his exasperation. Thus, when in bed with his wife later, he experienced a number of conflicting feelings. He wanted to demonstrate his real love for his wife, who was obviously sexually willing; yet his suppressed anger was pushing for expression, which would have made him feel guilty. He went ahead with the sexual preliminaries and had no difficulty with erection until his wife happened to mention the good time she had had at the party. This comment triggered a sudden loss of his erection, which, as he explained to himself and his wife, was probably due to fatigue and too much to drink. These excuses might indeed have been contributing factors along with the other internal pressures of anger, love and guilt. At this point, one might wonder why he didn't choose to express his annoyance and get things settled with his wife in open discussion. Here the plot thickens, as further previously unconscious motives came to light. He became aware that he envied the success and appearance of the friend who had been too attentive to his wife and that he felt inferior and unable to compete with him. Thus, his impotence not only expresses anger, love and guilt in relation to his wife, but also inferiority and passive submission to his friend, as if he were almost proclaiming that his wife might be better satisfied by his friend than by himself.

This example demonstrates the range of external and internal factors contributing to this bit of human behavior. We might conceive of a complemental series consisting of these factors from direct reactions to physical and external stimuli, through conscious reality-oriented motives and feelings, to unconscious, irrational and primitive forces. When the latter predominate in the form of fixed psychopathology, the sexual dysfunction that expresses it may be quite persistent, inasmuch as it serves as a vehicle of expression for these unconscious pressures, otherwise denied access to behavior. On the other hand, if deep psychological conflict does not contribute in a major way to the impotence, it is likely to be a superficial and transient reaction to an immediate stress.

An example of a state intermediate between these two extremes would be that of a man who, although having unresolved sexual conflicts, may have no obvious dysfunction when young and under greater urgency and sexual pressure, which overrides inhibitions. However, as sexual urgency diminishes with age and the psychological problems of middle age join forces with the pre-existing conflicts, impotence is more likely to occur.

There is a further complication that might occur in those men who, in spite of considerable psychopathology, have maintained an equilibrium without symptoms. If an episode of impotence occurs for a relatively superficial reason, such as drinking to excess or fear of discovery, this episode may act like a match in a tinderbox, and the traumatic failure undermines his precarious masculine confidence. The fear of another failure may join forces with latent fears to prompt a withdrawal and panicky retreat. Such cases require prompt medical and psychological counseling to restore confidence and prevent further regression to a fixed symptomatic state, or if this has occurred, judicious psychotherapy such as Masters and Johnson describe may be sufficient to re-establish the equilibrium that existed before. An important factor is the support by physician and wife, which shores up the damaged confidence of the patient until successful sexual performance restores it again.

If I were to limit myself to the title of my paper and discuss only psychoanalytic treatment of male sexual dysfunction, I would have little to say of a specific nature. Psychoanalysis as a therapy aims, not at the cure of a single symptom, but rather at nothing less than a far-reaching exploration and reorientation of the total personality. If a man were to seek treatment for an acute problem of impotence, with no evidence of other psychopathology, I would not recommend psychoanalysis. If, as is the more usual case in practice, he has other symptoms, such as phobias, obsessions or characterological distortions such as difficulties in his dealings with people, analysis might then be considered. In addition to the signs and symptoms of psychopathology, there are important considerations such as the realities of time and money, judgment of severity of illness, intellectual capacity, motivation and ability to sustain a difficult and often painful search for and correction of hidden conflicts, ingrained habits and restrictions. Psychoneurosis represents a process that has developed over many years, and psychoanalytic treatment attempts to reverse that process by providing a situation wherein the complicated disguises of inner conflict can be experienced and understood with increasing clarity and then subjected to the influence of mature logic and experience. This change cannot be accomplished by a narrow concentration on one symptom, requiring instead a free-ranging scrutiny of any and all aspects of the personality as determined by the most pressing psychic forces of any given moment. It is always found that there exist numerous connections and common derivations of symptoms, attitudes and behavior that seem unrelated superficially.

It can be seen readily that this treatment should not be lightly invoked. To use it for relatively simple psychological problems has been compared to using an elephant gun on a mouse. At the other extreme are mental illnesses where the personality is so deformed and the capacity to cooperate so impaired that the psychoanalytic method cannot be applied except in modified form. Thus, as a treatment method, psychoanalysis has definite limitations and has its greatest usefulness in the understanding of human psychic functioning. This understanding can then be applied in the treatment of conditions not usually acceptable for or in need of the classical psychoanalytic method. One of the best examples of such application of analytic knowledge was by Freud himself when in 1910 he was consulted by Gustav Mahler, who was afflicted with impotence. In a period of four hours during which they strolled through a park, Freud helped Mahler understand how his impotence was due to his unconscious confusion of his wife with his mother, both of whom were named Marie. In view of the picture of childhood typical of men with sexual dysfunction sketched earlier in this paper, it is interesting that Mahler was very close to his mother, who dominated his life, and feared his father, who was described as a brutal person. Mahler recovered his potency and had no more sexual difficulty for the rest of his life.

Undoubtedly, an important factor in this rapid symptomatic cure was that Mahler, according to Freud, had an amazing intuitive grasp of psychological processes. However, anyone dealing with the problem of impotence, be he physician, priest or witch doctor, can tell of similar rapid cures, which is not surprising in view of what has been said previously of the shifting balance of psychic forces in the human mind. When that balance has been upset, the healer's job is to restore it by removing the weight, counterbalancing it or strengthening the resistance to it. Even without the intervention of any form of treatment, natural healing takes place through maturation, acts of fate, beginning new relationships or ending old ones. If we examine such cures, either spontaneous or induced by some form of therapy, we will find that the impotence that resulted from an interaction of a number of psychological pressures has been displaced from its position in the equilibrium. It may be replaced by a substitute symptom, such as an avoidance of all or certain women or perhaps a counterphobic promiscuity that does not really test the man's masculinity, a supportive relationship with a person or an institution, or, more fortunately, a psychic maturation and experiential growth.

If I now attempt a psychoanalytic explanation of why Masters and Johnson's therapy of impotence has a high rate of success, it is with the suspicion that they have intuitively understood and knowingly utilized many of these principles of psychic functioning. They have realized that in addition to any individual psychopathology each partner in a sexually troubled marriage may have, there is likely to be a neurotic equilibrium set up that involves them both. Masters and Johnson have sensed the regressive reactivation of latent fears by current stress and fear of failure, starting a vicious cycle of failure, fear, loss of confidence and withdrawal into mutual distress. They understand the need for detailed revelation of the sexual problem, not only for the facts but also for ventilation and the establishment of mutual trust and cooperation between the therapeutic team and the married couple, as well as a renewal of trust and cooperation between husband and wife. I am sure that they have grasped fully the several purposes served by teaching anatomical facts and stimulative techniques, which not only overcome inexperience and provide a sense of mastery through knowledge but also serve at least a temporarily magical function of giving confidence. I am reminded in this regard of Walt Disney's story of Dumbo, the flying elephant, who had been given a magic feather to enable him to fly. He at first attributed his talent to the feather, only to discover that he had been flying under his own power all the time and could do so without the magic. I believe that once confidence in potency is restored by success, some of the dependence on the magical meaning of certain techniques may be outgrown and that the couple may not need the psychological support that they represent.

This observation brings me to what may be the most important factor in sustaining the success that this method as well as many others may achieve. This factor is the potential for growth that is too often ignored, even by psychiatrists and analysts who should know better. Perhaps the fact that they deal with the more severe, fixed cases of impotence acts to obscure an awareness that people do grow and change spontaneously, often overcoming symptoms or at least developing less disabling types of symptoms. Those individuals whose psychopathology is not too pervasive have personality resources that may be tapped by growth-promoting experiences, which may help resolve some inner conflicts or may strengthen the ability to contain or compensate for those conflicts that remain.

From my knowledge of the Masters and Johnson method, it appears to me that an important basis for their success lies in their selection process. Couples who apply for this treatment must have strong motivation as evidenced both by their willingness to undergo the treatment process and by their ability to cooperate with each other. This motivation is tested not only in initial selection but also at least at one point after the initial interviewing and during discussion of the plan of treatment. Couples whose capacity to cooperate further is impaired by doubts about the basic solidity of the marriage or by neurotic problems are screened out, leaving only those who are highly motivated and likely to have the most growth potential.

Working with this select group and utilizing a team approach to interrupt a pathological interaction between the partners by powerful psychological forces of ventilation, persuasion, permission, identification and education makes it understandable that this approach is able to help many sexually troubled marriages. The element of group sanction and pressure from the therapeutic team and spouse exerts strong influence on the sexually inadequate patient, counteracting inhibitions, fears and taboos. This influence gives permission to override prohibitions and sets up new standards of approved behavior. The duration of this change will depend on the extent to which the reward of mutual sexual satisfaction, the sense of mastery and the gain in self-esteem can be integrated into a new growth-promoting experience, as opposed to the persistence of intrapsychic conflict that resists change with favorable experience. The patients who do achieve a lasting gain in sexual performance are probably those who are "ripe" for growth and change, whereas those who are too burdened by inhibition, anxiety and hostility do not have the necessary investment in their marriage or are unable to cooperate and complete the prescribed course of treatment.

This approach takes its place alongside other methods, such as brief psychotherapy for acute sexual problems and psychoanalysis for serious ones. It seems indicated for those married couples whose problem will not yield to the usual counseling or brief psychotherapy and who are highly motivated, cooperative and not too crippled by psychopathology. Individuals with powerful intrapsychic conflict and rigid defenses and those whose goals are not only sexual potency but also a far-reaching personality reorientation will continue to seek psychoanalysis.

6

PSYCHOANALYTIC MEANING AND TREATMENT OF FRIGIDITY

Burness E. Moore, M.D.

Dr. Burness E. Moore is a training analyst at the New York Psychoanalytic Institute.

THE DEVELOPMENT OF THE MIND AND A SENSE OF SEXUAL IDENTITY

Derived at first from adult analyses but later verified by direct observation of infants and children, a large body of evidence supports the conclusion that developmentally psychic functioning follows the model of bodily functions. The mind introjects—i.e., takes in, as in nursing—what is need-satisfying and pleasurable and seeks to evacuate what is noxious or unpleasant. The gratification of physiological needs by the mother establishes memory traces of the satisfying experience, which are reactivated in a wish-fulfilling way when, as it inevitably happens, the mother is unable to satisfy them immediately. This progression from appreciation of need to the psychic state after satisfaction, even when the need has not been met, has the anticipatory quality of a conditioned reflex, but it is the beginning of fantasy and thought. The mother comes to recognize the meaning of her infant's motor

PSYCHOANALYTIC MEANING AND TREATMENT OF FRIGIDITY:
From *Sexual Function and Dysfunction*, edited by Paul Jay Fink, M.D., and Van Buren O. Hammett, M.D. Copyright © 1969 by F. A. Davis Company. Reprinted by permission of the author, editors and publisher.

activity and emotions, and her appreciation of and response to these preverbal signals establishes a primitive affecto-motor form of communication between them. The degree of satisfaction in this interchange probably contributes to the capacity for empathy and other qualities in later life. A similar nonverbal communication is an important component in the sexual act.

The body image is gradually built up by the amalgamation of memory traces of sensations, produced by stimuli, some from the physiological processes of the body and some from the ministrations of the first emotionally charged object, the mother. Psychic representations of other people are at first only partial, with the breast, face, hands and warmth of the body representing the mother. In the beginning, self and object representations are also poorly differentiated, and even in adult life they remain somewhat fluid and interchangeable.

From the age of about two to three years, the child passes through a phase, described by M. Mahler as "separation-individuation," during which the psychic conception of the self is established as separate from the object. Even then satiation predisposes to fusion of self and object representations and returns to a psychic state similar to the earlier unity with mother, while deprivation heightens the sense of separation. If the mother has not provided the infant with an optimal degree of instinctual gratification and frustration, graded to the needs and strength of the child's developing mind, individuation and the development of a sense of self and identity are impaired. The very identity of the individual is therefore determined in part by the degree of gratification of instinctual needs he finds in relation to other people, mother and father most importantly in early life, and by the conflicts connected with the gratification that may interfere with or facilitate identification with the parent of the same sex. All individuals have some admixture of masculine and feminine qualities derived from identification with both parents. Problems of sexual function may be the result of unconscious sexual confusion, conflicts over the expression of sexual and aggressive drives arising because of internalized parental attitudes, or events that were traumatic in reality or merely because they were experienced at crucial stages of psychic development.

THE STAGES OF PSYCHOSEXUAL DEVELOPMENT

Freud believed that sexuality must be viewed developmentally. He regarded it as a broad concept, related to the function of obtaining pleasure from zones of the body—a function only later brought into the service of reproduction and under the primary dominance of the genitals. The mouth is the first erotogenic zone, receiving not only the nourishment necessary for self-preservation but also providing a satisfaction and pleasure independent of that function. With frustration of wishes, aggression is mobilized in the form of sadistic impulses, which begin to appear during the oral phase with the appearance of teeth and increase greatly in the second psychosexual phase, an anal stage during which satisfaction occurs in aggression and in the attainment of mastery over the excretory functions. This very aggression, which has a muscular component, too, aids the child in the process of separation-individuation, inasmuch as it often must engage in a struggle with mother to gain control over its own sphincter musculature. In sadism, Freud conceived of a fusion between libidinal and aggressive instinctual drives, thereafter a combined force that continues throughout the life of the individual. It is the source of an ambivalence of feeling toward all objects—simultaneous feelings of love and hostility—one part of which is usually only partially conscious.

P. McLean has presented neuroanatomical and physiological evidence in connection with the limbic system of the brain that supports Freud's theoretical formulations. Stimulation of the septum and related structures verifies the fact that penile erection is represented in cortical areas as well as in limbic nuclear structures connected with the cortex. Because of the close neural relationship between parts of the limbic system, excitation of one part readily spills over into another. The amygdala and septal pathways for oral and genital responses converge in the region of the hypothalamus, which Hess and others have shown to be of central importance in the expression of angry, combative and fearful behavior. These neurophysiologic findings contribute an understanding of the primitive interplay of oral and sexual behavior as well as their connection with aggressive behavior. The association of feeding with penile erection in babies and animals exemplifies this relationship.

Also consistent with these neurophysiologic findings and clinical observations is Freud's assumption of a third psychosexual stage, the phallic, during which both sexes are primarily aware of only the male genital. From neurophysiological and clinical evidence, we know that penile and clitoral arousal takes place in connection with the nursing experience. Fantasy substitution of the clitoris and penis for the erect nipple contributes to the unconscious equation of "clitoris—nipple (breast)—penis." Although P. Greenacre has reviewed the evidence showing that Freud was mistaken in his assumption that vaginal sensation and awareness are absent in the little girl, it is agreed that vaginal sensations at this period are vague, diffuse and poorly differentiated from those of the surrounding pelvic organs, especially the anus, with which the vagina shares a cloacal origin. Therefore, Freud was apparently right in attributing greater importance to clitoral interest in the girl child during the phallic period. Seeing the penis often arouses in the little girl an unconscious sense of an inadequacy in her equipment and an envy that may in later years be displaced from the original object and find expression in various character traits, such as jealousy and bitter competitiveness with men. Psychoanalysts call this behavior the "masculinity complex," and its intensity plays an important role in some cases of frigidity.

THE ROLE OF THE CLITORIS IN FEMALE SEXUALITY

The clitoris continues to play an important role in female sexuality throughout life. In his *Three Essays on the Theory of Sexuality,* Freud stated in 1905 that, "when at last the sexual act is permitted and the clitoris itself becomes excited, it still retains a function: the task, namely, of transmitting the excitation to the adjacent female sexual parts, just as— to use a simile—pine shavings can be kindled in order to set a log of harder wood on fire." He again reaffirmed the importance of the clitoris in his last paper on female sexuality in 1933, thus presaging the observations of Masters and Johnson. Nevertheless, Freud and others have shown that interest in the gratification provided by the clitoris undergoes many shifts in the course of female development. In childhood, its stimulation is disappointing and is given up. Interest in it shifts to a narcissistic concern with the girl's whole body. Disappointment in the wish for a penis in addition to other frustrations contributes to a shift in libidinal feeling from the mother to the father, and the wish for a penis is eventually replaced by the wish for a child. The father is the first male person to whom the girl child transfers the affection at first directed solely toward her mother. If this attachment is disappointing, it may give rise to a return to the masculinity complex with permanent impairment of her sexuality. In usual development, mother is given up as a love object through identification with her. This identification requires a passive, receptive, feminine mental attitude, at least sexually, and disturbances in the relations with either parents or siblings may interfere with its acquisition.

It is apparent from the preceding discussion that the female child has two psychological tasks to accomplish not required of the boy in sexual development: the shift from clitoral to vaginal interest and a change in the sex of her object choice from that of the original love object, her mother. In part, these requirements account for her greater difficulty in achieving orgasm.

It is worthwhile to clarify what is meant by the psychoanalytic clitoral-vaginal transfer theory, inasmuch as some individuals, Mary Jane Sherfey and Judd Marmor in particular, feel that the work of Masters and Johnson invalidates this theory. If both clitoris and vagina are invariably involved in female orgasm, how can there be a distinction between a clitoral and a vaginal orgasm or clitoral fixation? Analysts as well as others have assumed that Freud's clitoral-vaginal transfer theory referred to erotic sensations and that it implied for mature female responsiveness the necessity for an orgasm experienced in the vagina itself. In fact, the description of orgasm by many women did coincide with this expectation, and there was a too ready assumption that the absence of vaginal sensation and orgasm was a hallmark of sexual and psychological pathology. Clinical experience indicated, however, that this association was not necessarily the case. As Helene Deutsch remarked, cases of very severe neurotic illness have been helped without eliminating this problem. Also, psychotic women and aggressive, masculine women experienced intense vaginal orgasm, while loving, giving, maternal and happy women did not, even though they felt fully gratified.

The statement by Freud that I have quoted indicates his recognition of the continuing importance of the clitoris in orgasm, and I believe his comment about the necessity for a shift from the clitoris to the vagina should be understood to refer to the cathexis attached to those organs. Cathexis means an investment of psychic interest, which may be conscious or unconscious. It is not possible without a psychic representation of the organ involved. The diffuse distribution of female erogenous zones, the small and partly concealed nature of the genitals and the uncertainty of the origin of sensations interfere with psychic representation and cathexis; and the mind's effort to define their location, boundaries and functions continues throughout life. Although the clitoris is aroused early in the nursing experience and therefore acquires psychic representation and cathexis, it is not until the anatomical and physiological changes of puberty have occurred, with development of the venous plexi of the female's pelvic organs, and stimulation by the penis in coitus that a more complete psychic representation of female structure and function can occur. Even then it cannot be expected that an anatomically precise differentiation between the vagina and the cryptic clitoral structures will be made. The latter are intimately connected with the clitoris itself but also partially envelop the lower third of the vagina. Although important, the anatomical and physiological facts are of less consequence than their psychic representation. Hysterical anesthesias, for example, conform not to the anatomical distribution of nerves but to the patient's erroneous concepts of the body. Inasmuch as the clitoris has a long history of psychic representation and cathexis before stimulation of the vagina, it seems logical to suppose that this fact would determine that the experience of orgasm might be clitoral for a long time.

In view of woman's reproductive function, which includes pregnancy, parturition, nursing and mothering, it seems logical that maximal feminine satisfaction requires that interest in the clitoris and the sensations it provides become secondary in the woman to a passive, receptive interest in receiving the penis and a child through her vagina. In fact, there is a strong need in both sexes to cathect the vagina as the organ of mature female sexual pleasure. This situation is essential for reproduction, and preference for vaginal or coital orgasm, as opposed to that stimulated by external manipulation of the clitoral system, has obvious adaptive advantage biologically. But this preference is a psychic phenomenon, an attitude or wish that may influence the way in which orgasm is experienced. Vicissitudes in individual development will determine whether sensation from the cryptic structures involved in orgasm are associated with the clitoris or the vagina in the psychic experience.

Some of the factors I have already mentioned interfere with the development of the mature attitude necessary for vaginal cathexis. They may determine a fixation or regression to the phallic phase in which interest in the clitoris is paramount, with a reawakening of feelings of inadequacy, jealousy and competitiveness toward the male and envy of his presumed advantages. Her biological equivalent of castration gives rise to hostile wishes for revenge in the girl with a masculinity complex. The hostile purpose may be directed at the organ itself or be displaced to its function, so that the aim is then to destroy the potency of the man. This displacement may find expression in a vaginismus that prevents intromission or the tendency to excite expectations and not fulfill them—the most usual pattern in frigidity. It should be stressed, however, that these attitudes permeate the entire marital situation and are not confined to the sexual act alone. In fact, some aggressive, masculine women compete with the man and unconsciously deny their own penisless state by an orgasm that seems to vie with that of the male. One such patient proudly informed me that she had an ejaculation.

OTHER FACTORS CONTRIBUTING TO FRIGIDITY

It is necessary to add other complex considerations about variations in the course of individual development that may contribute to frigidity. In the main, they have been derived from the work of Freud in the period between 1916 and 1932, when he formulated a comprehensive theory of female psychosexual development. They have been confirmed and expanded since by many psychoanalytic observers.

The erotogenic zones are passively awakened by the mother's care, but the aggressive drive, the development of motor function and the need for separation stimulate an active erotic interest normally possessed by male and female alike in varying degrees. In general, however, there is reason to believe that passivity is more typical of the feminine attitude in the sexual act, whereas her active aims are directed to the love and care of her children. Various factors, including identification with an active-erotic mother, may interfere with the development of the usual passive, feminine attitude, and a degree of activity in the love act that is threatening and inhibiting to her male partner may be necessary for certain women to achieve orgasm. Although many women remain attached to their mothers, others simply transfer that attachment to the father, changing objects but remaining passively fixated on the mother. In that case, inadequate identification with the mother, who remains an unconscious love object, may lead to physical rejection of sex, inability to achieve orgasm or failure to achieve psychic gratification from an orgasm that occurs physiologically.

There are many opportunities for small children to observe intimacies between father and mother, and the wish to be included and to be a participant in the love relationship is indicated in the almost universal desire of the child to get in bed with mother and father. Fantasies about what goes on between mother and father are related to the primary zone of erotic gratification during particular phases of psychosexual development. Arguments between parents, and especially physical conflict, are associated unconsciously with sexual activity and constitute the basis for sadomasochistic fantasies. These fantasies are related to the oral and anal sadistic impulses of the child and are integrated with fantasies explaining the difference between the sexes, including castration fears. A strongly persisting oedipal attachment to the "violent, overpowering father" may be repressed but gives rise to masochistic fantasies in the adult sexual relationship against which the woman may need to defend herself by frigidity. Orgasm, which involves a loss of motor and psychic control, is in these cases most often associated in the mind of the woman with those emotionally satisfying but frightening functions peculiar to her sex but over which she has relatively little conscious control—menstruation, with its bloody, messy implications; pregnancy; and the bloody, painful experience of childbirth. The masochistic concept of herself as castrated may be denied in some women by giving to the body itself the significance of a phallus. The narcissistic preoccupation with their bodies and self-interests of some women interfere with the object-directed interests and giving necessary for full sexual satisfaction. Their narcissism is sometimes transferred to their children as an extension of themselves, and they find such gratification in the active love and care they give to their children that there is little need for or interest in orgastic satisfaction with their husbands.

This discussion has dealt with bases for frigidity inherent in the psychosexual development of the individual woman. Although they have great importance, I can only mention the psychological problems of her sexual partner, the emotional interaction between them, the adequacy of stimulation, the influence of hormones, the circumstances under which intercourse takes place, and social and cultural attitudes toward sex that are other important factors affecting female orgastic potential. Although none of these factors can be neglected in the psychoanalytic view, psychoanalysis cannot change the realities of these factors but may influence the fate and effect of their representation in the mind by reducing conflicts that interfere with function. They are, nevertheless, factors that may seriously limit what can be accomplished by psychoanalysis in the treatment of frigidity, however much analysis may otherwise benefit the total functioning of the patient. As one simple example, I might point out that it is conceivable that an impaired orgastic response in the woman may be a more mature, realistic and adaptive reaction to her sexual mate than an overwhelming orgastic reaction that would be threatening to him and impair a tenuous but in other respects gratifying object relationship and satisfactory marriage.

The human sexual act is a profound and complex phenomenon. It is often initiated by nonverbal cues, preferably in a situation of emotional closeness as well as physical intimacy. It is preceded by foreplay that reawakens the interest or cathexis in earlier stages of psychosexual development as a build-up in erotic tension that is finally discharged in a genital union of two bodies. It is, therefore, a regressive act that returns the individual to the earliest oral stage, progresses back up to the genital level and culminates in an ecstatic symbolic fusion with the partner that momentarily repeats the earliest blissful state of union with the mother. This intertwining of physical and psychic elements in the act helps to account for some of the varieties of ways of achieving orgasm, as well as disturbances in function, frigidity especially. Events or human relationships that traumatize the child at particular stages of development account for the variations we see—arousal or even orgasm by stimulation of the nipples, the desire for anal intercourse, the need for stimulation of various parts of the body, sadomasochistic fantasies and even frigidity. In some patients I have seen, differentiation of the self from the object requires constant struggle. The sexual act implies a total regression; and orgasm, a loss of conscious control that threatens the insecure, unstably differentiated woman with a merging, a fusion with the sexual partner to the degree that her identity would be lost. Regardless of her conscious wishes for orgastic experience, frigidity is for such a woman a necessary, last-ditch defense against oblivion.

THE ROLE OF PSYCHOANALYSIS IN THE TREATMENT OF FRIGIDITY

My discussion has demonstrated, I believe, the tremendous complexity of orgastic experience. It is not simply a physical phenomenon, nor can it be dealt with solely by physical techniques, which is not to say that all women with frigidity require psychoanalysis. Like any other symptom, frigidity must have diagnostic evaluation and therapy directed toward the specific underlying causes. In cases of frigidity, psychoanalysis is indicated, I believe, primarily for those women whose accompanying neurosis includes a strong masculinity complex. If the problems it creates have produced conflict about which the patient is at least partially aware and for which she wants help, the outlook is favorable. For the reasons I have mentioned, some of the developmental vicissitudes of female development do not give rise to conflict.

Moreover, the erotic needs of some women find such gratification in their biological function of motherhood that specific orgastic discharge is not required or missed. In the case of some couples, internalized prohibitions about sex have prevented that degree of freedom to explore and experiment necessary to overcome ignorance of female anatomy and discover those techniques of stimulation and timing required for female orgasm. For them, a modified approach based on the educational and training techniques described by Masters and Johnson may be rewarding.

A description of the psychoanalytic technique for treatment of frigidity would be beyond the scope of this chapter. I will say only a few words about psychoanalytic treatment in general. Although we have a consciousness that makes us aware of certain perceptions of the external world and of our bodies and minds, it is fleeting in duration, and percepts are stored as memories, the recall of which is notably subject to conflict. Images, ideas and feelings connected with experiences that have given rise to fantasies expressing forbidden sexual and aggressive wishes encounter a repression or form of censorship, which keeps them from coming to conscious awareness. The mental processes by which perception, memories and the defenses against them affect the body are no more within our awareness than the neurological or metabolic activities of the brain. Derivatives of their presence do find expression, however, in thought associations, fantasies, feelings, dreams and action. The analytic situation encourages a transient regression in which these derivatives find expression in relation to the analyst as a relatively anonymous person to whom feelings toward important objects in the past are transferred. This fact aids the analyst in recognizing or reconstructing past events and the conflicts associated with them, and by interpretation they are brought into consciousness. Their effect is modified by the integration of the past with the present.

By breaking down the barriers of defense and resistance to phenomona of perception and memory, based on conflict, which determine the unconscious quality of some of these manifestations, there is an enrichment of the total personality. Bound energies become freed, neutralized and therefore available for the synthetic and integrating functions of the mind.

The imposed necessity for relinquishment of action facilitates the transfer of energies from the motoric aspects of behavior to the symbolic, thus improving the capacity to institute delay, postpone gratification and tolerate frustration, all essential elements in the development of a mature person, capable of loving and being loved.

Psychoanalytic treatment is not generally available nor is it indicated for all patients with frigidity. Its principal value is in the deeper understanding it provides with respect to the complexities of human behavior. With due respect for those complexities, useful principles may be derived from its findings and applied to the handling of sexual problems by other doctors. The causes of frigidity are far more likely to be psychic than physical; and neurotic conflict, ignorance of anatomy and poor techniques of stimulation and timing are the most frequent contributory factors, the last two often determined by the first. Nevertheless, for many patients with psychological problems, treatment in a medical setting is more acceptable than psychiatric therapy. Without altering one's fundamental role as a physician—indeed by virtue of it—it is possible to give effective psychological help.

I have mentioned already the necessity for careful diagnostic appraisal of the marital and sexual situation. One or more long talks with both sexual partners are necessary to determine the nature of the sexual problem and their attitudes toward each other. Sometimes an interview with the two together will reveal more about the emotional interaction between them than separate discussion; for example, the active or passive role assumed by each, their competitiveness and need to dominate and control, attitudes that have a sadistic or masochistic implication, the tendency to accept or project blame, the degree of concern of each for the other's happiness and satisfaction, their motivation to solve their problems and the willingness of both partners to cooperate in efforts to work together toward that aim. Unless there is sufficient motivation for both parties to cooperate wholeheartedly, the efforts of the physician are not likely to meet with success.

The most important instruments of the physician in helping these patients are transference, objectivity and knowledge. Transference refers to the patient's tendency to transfer to the doctor important attitudes and feelings derived from earlier object relationships, usually those with mother and father during childhood. It takes place almost universally and in the case of sexual problems will usually imply an attitude of respect as well as an expectation of condemnation and disapproval of sexual wishes and a sense of relief with relaxation of tension and euphoria when that expectation is not fulfilled. The mere fact that the physician listens with respect and sympathy to a woman's problems, approves her efforts to achieve and give sexual satisfaction and wishes to be helpful is of tremendous aid in some cases. The attachment to the father is perhaps never as completely resolved in women as is the oedipal complex in men, and the participation of an oedipal figure, the physician, in helping her obtain sexual pleasure probably provides a powerful stimulation in unconscious fantasy to some women, sufficient to break through the barriers to orgastic discharge. On the other hand, lack of objectivity or too much warmth may inhibit rather than help by threatening a realistic achievement of such forbidden fantasy.

For this reason it is vitally important that the physician maintain the same objectivity he would in respect to physical pathology. Whatever his own standards of behavior and modes of sexual gratification, he must avoid being judgmental or condemnatory and instead must exercise tolerance and respect for the patient's needs and views. This attitude includes approaching the problem without preconceived ideas about the proper nature and intensity of female orgasm, a fallacy from which the patient is often suffering already. There is far greater variation in female sexual response and orgasm than in male, even though the same physiological reactions may occur. Under the best of circumstances, even fully orgastic women do not achieve orgasm all the time. A more relaxed attitude about what is expected is often helpful in frigidity as in impotence.

This information about the diversity of responses and the acceptability of the woman's own reactions is only part of the physician's knowledge, which his authoritative role as a transference figure enables him to use effectively. Many patients, both male and female, have only the vaguest idea of female anatomy due to the unconscious conflicts that have prevented exploration and learning. Previous ideas about the appropriate male and female roles may need to be contradicted and satisfaction of her own and her partner's needs and wishes placed first. This change involves some instruction in the need for verbal communication between the two partners. Many women are angrily disappointed that their husbands do not know how they wish to be stimulated and fail to recognize their own inhibition about telling them.

The objective of such treatment is not simply the attainment of a physical orgasm but also the improvement of the total emotional relationship between the sexual partners. It is training in tender, loving consideration for each other's needs, without which orgasm will remain elusive or, if it occurs, will be only a meaningless and unfulfilling narcissistic experience.

7

A NEUROSIS IS 'JUST' A BAD HABIT

Morton M. Hunt

The recipe for Masters and Johnson's therapy is so many parts of dual-sex-team counseling, so many parts of behavior therapy, a pinch of personality, a cup of charisma and who knows how many other elements deriving their flavor from the unique interaction of these two complex individuals. The only one of these elements that has been adequately described in writing outside of Masters and Johnson's own literary efforts is behavior therapy—and it must be stressed that the St. Louis scientists have so completely adapted this form of psychotherapy to their own methods that it is scarcely recognizable as they apply it. Nonetheless, an understanding of behavior therapy can provide insight into the relearning process that's involved in all of the Reproductive Biology Research Foundation therapies.

Morton Hunt, the author of this chapter, is one of the English language's most prolific and respected writers on subjects involving human behavior. His many books include A Natural History of Love, Her Infinite Variety, The World of the Formerly Married *and* The Affair.

Psychoanalytic treatment of the neurotic patient, though usually protracted, distressing and expensive, is at least flattering—it rests on the premises that the patient's psyche is intricate and subtle and that his neurosis is the result of arcane, intractable and complicated conflicts. But a radically different view is beginning to gain ground in some circles of contemporary psychology. Most unflatteringly, it holds that psychologically we human beings are not much different from cats, rats or dogs.

It declares that the "unconscious" is either nonexistent or at best irrelevant and that even the most complicated neuroses are nothing but faulty conditioning which can—as with the lower animals—be easily changed, by training, in a tenth or twentieth of the time taken by analytic therapy, and without soul-searching or probing for insight.

The leading investigator and proponent of this school of "behavior therapy" (or "learning therapy" or "conditioning therapy") is Dr. Joseph Wolpe, 52, a short, baldish South African psychiatrist, who is now a professor at Temple University's School of Medicine in Philadelphia. Dr. Wolpe's dissent from the dominant Freudian tradition is total. "There is no scientific evidence for the Freudian conception of neurosis as the result of a repressed complex," he says. "Contrary to the popular psychoanalytic conception, a neurosis is 'just' a habit—a persistent habit of unadaptive behavior, acquired by learning."

Wolpe is not alone. Harvard's B. F. Skinner, the University of London's H. J. Eysenck, and perhaps a couple of hundred less famous psychologists and psychiatrists (most of them in the U.S. and England) say much the same thing. Eysenck, the best-known gadfly of Freudianism, flatly asserts that there is no need to postulate unconscious causes for neurotic symptoms—indeed, a neurosis, according to him, is nothing but its own symptoms. "Get rid of the symptoms," he says, "and you have eliminated the neurosis." (Freudians, of course, say that unless you get rid of the hidden conflicts,

A NEUROSIS IS "JUST" A BAD HABIT:
Originally appeared in the June 4, 1967, issue of The New York Times Magazine. Copyright © 1967 by Morton M. Hunt. Reprinted by permission of the author.

they will only produce other symptoms in place of the eliminated ones.)

How do Wolpe and other behavior therapists get rid of symptoms and thus, presumably, of the entire neurosis? Here are a few typical scenes of behavior therapy in progress:

A thin, tense-looking 18-year-old boy sits in a chair at one end of a long room and makes himself relax as completely as possible. He suffers from a compulsive need to wash, spending hours a day at it because of his fear of contaminating himself or others with his own urine; he had been forced to sleep with his sister until he was 15, a situation in which, a psychoanalyst might suggest, he unconsciously substituted urine in his thoughts for the semen with which he feared to contaminate her.

The therapist now brings into the far end of the room a stoppered bottle of urine; the boy raises one hand (as per instruction) to indicate that its presence is making him anxious. The therapist tells him to relax his entire body and to concentrate on "letting go"; after a while he is no longer anxious, and the therapist then brings the bottle a bit closer. Again the boy feels anxious; again he is helped to relax.

In later sessions he will even be able to handle the bottle; still later he will allow the doctor to put a very diluted drop of urine in water on the back of his hand; still later a more concentrated drop; and eventually a full-strength drop. The goal is to associate the relaxed state—which counteracts anxiety—with the presence of urine; gradually this should condition away the boy's habitual fear of urine and eliminate his symptoms.

* * *

A 35-year-old homosexual man sits in a darkened room with an electrode strapped to his calf. A picture of a nude man is illuminated before him, while a steady, painful shock is applied to his calf; after a short while the picture goes dark, a different picture—of a nude woman—is lit up and the electric shock stops. The hope is that the homosexual stimulus will be associated with, and hence inhibited by, the painful shock, while the heterosexual stimulus will be rewardingly associated with the pleasurable cessation of the pain. This, it is hoped, will turn the patient into a heterosexual.

* * *

A businessman sits facing his therapist and speaks in a rambling and repetitious manner; again and again he voices thoughts, which he cannot escape, that fire will destroy his warehouse and his company, though in fact his warehouse and contents are physically well protected and thoroughly insured. Suddenly the doctor shouts, "Stop!" In the ensuing silence, he quietly points out to the startled patient that the shout did actually interrupt the perseverating thoughts. He asks the patient to start talking again about his business; the patient does so, and when he gets back to the subject of fire, the doctor again shouts at him. After several rounds of this, the doctor instructs him to interrupt such thoughts in the future, at any time and place, by mentally shouting, "Stop!" at himself, until eventually the thoughts themselves automatically trigger off their own termination.

The philosophy underlying behavior therapy is not new; it is a resurgence of behaviorism (the psychology espoused by Pavlov in Russia and by C. L. Hull, J. B. Watson, E. L. Thorndike and others in America), which flowered briefly about 40 years ago but was then quite overshadowed in the United States by Freudian psychology. With behaviorism (or "learning theory," as the neo-Pavlovians prefer to call it) reviving, certain of its adherents, most notably Wolpe, have been developing new therapeutic methods based upon it.

Behavior therapy is so new and so radical that until a year or so ago there was no place in the United States to get training in it, but in 1966 Wolpe began a program of research and training at Temple University, and a nonprofit clinic and training center called the Behavior Therapy Institute opened in Sausalito, California. Since 1963 the movement has had an international journal, *Behavior Research and Therapy*, and the American Psychiatric Association had Wolpe speak on the subject at its 1966 annual meeting.

The great majority of American psychotherapists, being partly or wholly committed to Freudian theory, are either contemptuous of or horrified by the theory and practice of behavior therapists, since the latter regard their patients as not altogether unlike laboratory animals that can be made ill or well by subjecting them to habit-forming or habit-erasing drills and routines.

The theoretical rationale of the behavior therapists has

its origins in the experimental work with dogs that Pavlov began early in the century. Every college student is familiar with his classic work in conditioning, from which he developed a psychology according to which all behavior—normal and abnormal—is viewed as a series of learned stimulus-response association. Pavlov believed that abnormal behavior was the result of conflicting conditioning, and he supported this view with an experiment: Having trained a dog to expect food when it saw a circle and no food when it saw an oval, he then made the oval more and more nearly circular until the dog, no longer able to distinguish between them, abruptly went berserk, whining, struggling, biting and howling. American experimenters, beginning in the late 1920s, followed Pavlov's lead. By associating shocks or air blasts with feeding, or by training an animal to do something to get a reward and then switching the colors or signals he had learned, they produced all sorts of neurotic behavior—rage, indigestion, sleeplessness, agitation, immobility.

Wolpe, a general practitioner studying psychiatry at the University of Witwatersrand in Johannesburg in 1947 and 1948, read the Pavlovian literature and repeated some of these experiments with variations of his own. He made several cats neurotic by giving them electric shocks while feeding them in a cage in the experiment room; eventually, they refused to eat in that cage, even after days of starvation and long after the shocks had been discontinued. Wolpe then sought to reverse the conditioning—that is, to "cure" the neurotic cats by dissociating their fear from the feeding situation. First, he offered them food pellets in a room which only remotely resembled the one in which they had been made neurotic; with their anxiety at a minimum, they easily learned to eat in a cage in that room. He then did the same thing in a second room rather more like the experiment room, then in a third, and finally in the experiment room itself.

He called this method "reciprocal inhibition" and later formally put it in these words: "If a response inhibitory of anxiety can be made to occur in the presence of anxiety-provoking stimuli, it will weaken the bond between these stimuli and the anxiety." The pleasurable response has to be stronger than the anxiety felt; the anxiety-provoking stimuli therefore have to be tackled in sequence, the weakest first and the stronger ones later. His therapeutic method assumes that neurosis—in man as well as in the cat—is nothing but a set of maladaptive habits, built into the brain in the form of connections between the neurons, or brain cells—connections that can be dismantled by routine training.

The feeding response was strong enough and pleasurable enough to overcome anxiety in his cats, but Wolpe realized that it would rarely be so for human beings—nor would it be easily manageable in office practice. He therefore sought for some response that would have more meaning and be more easily usable. After some years of experimenting and reading, he came upon the idea which is at the heart of nearly three quarters of all therapy he does today: If the patient can be taught to relax all his muscles very completely, the automatic nervous system will convey throughout his system a set of physical conditions that oppose the feeling of anxiety—and if this relaxed, antianxious state can be associated with a fear-inducing stimulus, it will countercondition the stimulus and render it innocuous. (This is true only of neurotic fear, where the stimulus does not actually represent a real and continuing danger.)

The muscle-relaxation method he evolved is called systematic desensitization. Before starting a patient upon a course of such treatment, Wolpe spends a few hours getting the patient's history, administering personality tests and orienting the patient to the idea that his neurosis is only one or more habits conditioned in him by experience—and rather easily replaceable by new habits, without any need to dig into "ultimate" childhood causes.

He then begins to train the patient in deep muscle relaxation, using a shortened version of a method described by Dr. Edmund Jacobson in 1938. This involves systematic practice in "letting go" of muscle groups—first in the forehead, then the face, and so on down the body. At first a patient may need as much as 15 minutes of concentrated effort to fully let go of any one muscle group—but later can attain complete relaxation of the whole body in a matter of minutes.

While the patient is learning this procedure, Wolpe and he are also constructing one or more "hierarchies" (graded lists) of anxiety-arousing stimuli. According to Wolpe and other behavior therapists, nearly any neurosis, no matter how complex, can be analyzed into a finite set of phobialike responses to specific "stimulus antecedents"—scenes, objects or situations which trigger off anxiety and all its concomitant aberrations and symptoms. A hierarchy is a group of such stimuli with a common theme; the specific themes and the individual stimuli are, of course, unique for each patient.

Mrs. C. W., a housewife of 52, came to Wolpe because of overpowering fears of rejection, illness and death, and a host of symptoms stemming from these feelings; here are two of the three hierarchies he and she constructed, the stimulus antecedents being listed in the order of their diminishing effect in producing anxiety:

FEAR OF DEATH

1. First husband in his coffin
2. At a burial
3. Seeing a burial assemblage from afar
4. Obituary notice of young person dying of a heart attack
5. Driving past a cemetery
6. Seeing a funeral (the nearer, the worse)
7. Passing a funeral home
8. Obituary notice of old person (worse if died of heart disease)
9. Inside a hospital
10. Seeing a hospital
11. Seeing an ambulance

FEAR OF SYMPTOMS
(despite knowing them to be nonsignificant)

1. Extrasystoles [irregular heartbeats]
2. Shooting pains in chest and abdomen
3. Pains in left shoulder and back
4. Pain on top of head
5. Buzzing in ears
6. Tremor of hands
7. Numbness or pain in fingertips
8. Difficulty in breathing after exertion
9. Pain in left hand (old injury)

This timid, dependent, hypochondrial woman would seem

to most Freudian therapists to require long-term insight therapy, since her symptoms appear to be a set of defenses against hostility and death wishes that her superego would not permit her to recognize. Wolpe regards such diagnoses as speculative, quasi-mystical and valueless. His own approach was simply to desensitize the patient to each item on the list, one by one. Having got her deeply relaxed, he would proceed about as follows (this being part of her 17th desensitization session; in previous sessions he had conquered items 9 to 4 on her Fear of Symptoms hierarchy):

"I am going to present a number of scenes to your imagination which you will imagine very clearly. First, we are going to have something already well familiar to you at these sessions—a pain 'n your left shoulder. [In previous sessions she had reported being slightly disturbed at imagining this.] You will imagine this pain very clearly and you will not be at all disturbed. (*Pause of about four seconds*) Stop imagining this pain and again concentrate on your relaxing. (*Pause of about 15 seconds*) Now again imagine that you have this pain in your left shoulder. (*Pause of about ten seconds*) Stop imagining the pain and again relax. (*Pause of about 15 seconds*) Now I'd like you to imagine the pain in your left shoulder a third time, very clearly and calmly. (*Pause of about 10 seconds*) Now stop this pain and focus your attention on your body, on the pleasant, relaxed feeling you have. [The patient later reported that the first presentation of the imagined pain had slightly disturbed her, but by the third presentation it had not disturbed her at all.]

By this curiously simple—or seemingly simple—method, Wolpe has been able, according to his own testimony, to overcome not only simple classic phobias but all sorts of complex neurotic conditions, including compulsive behavior, social inadequacy, character neuroses, and so on—usually in about one twentieth the therapeutic time required by psychoanalytically oriented therapies. Even such classically difficult disorders as extreme aversion to sexual relations are usually easily curable, in Wolpe's view. A young woman came to him recently with just such feelings, which were wrecking her marriage. Though she said many things that seemed to indicate deep ambivalence between a desire to be loving to her husband and a fear of being dominated by him, Wolpe saw no need to examine these subjects with her in protracted discussions. Instead, he went about identifying the immediate stimulus antecedents of her anxiety—all of them being situations involving the sight or touch of the penis.

He and the patient then worked out a hierarchy which began with an imagined scene in which she saw a nude marble statue of a man from a distance of 50 feet; the mild anxiety she felt at imagining herself seeing the marble penis from this distance was desensitized by the effects of deep relaxation, after which Wolpe moved her, in imagination, to 30 feet away, then to ten, then right next to the statue.

Next he had her imagine various scenes of her husband in the nude, coming closer to her and in physical intimacy with her. At last reports, she was able in real life to begin actual experiencing of the sight, nearness and touch that she had learned to tolerate in imagination and was starting to experience pleasure in sex.

Even if such procedures do really reduce the anxiety felt while imagining scenes in the office, one may well ask why this kind of practice should automatically carry over and reduce anxiety in real-life situations.

Wolpe asserts that there is indeed an equivalence between the imaginary stimulus and the real one and that to neutralize the former is to neutralize the latter. Until there is some independent evaluation of the results he and other behavior therapists have reported, the interested outsider will have to take their word for it that it does happen—and hope that it does; the future would surely be brighter for all neurotics if it were really so.

A systematic desensitization is the treatment of choice for about 70 percent of Wolpe's patients. The rest need, in addition or instead, any one of a number of other conditioning therapies that Wolpe and others have devised in the past decade. One such method is what Wolpe calls "assertive training," a technique first popularized by Andrew Salter, a New York psychologist of Pavlovian sympathies. Simply stated, it consists of encouraging and even rehearsing the patient in asserting himself, expressing his views and particularly speaking out his angry feelings against people who criticize or misuse him. According to Wolpe's theorizing, the total physical mood created by speaking out one's feelings

of this sort acts as a counterforce to anxiety; it thus conditions away the fear felt in the presence of the bully or
domineering person.

With a timid man, for instance, who deserved promotion
but was afraid to ask for it, Wolpe, a normally soft-spoken
man, enacted the role of the harsh, loud-voiced employer,
while the patient acted himself coming in to ask for the
promotion. Having gone through the skit once, Wolpe seated
the patient at his place at the desk and play-acted the patient's timid, hesitant manner entering the room; he then
replayed the scene as an assertive individual; and finally,
resuming his place behind the desk, rehearsed the patient
several times in his new role until he felt comfortable in it.
The patient got his promotion.

Most other cases are more complicated—patients are
trained in talking back to their parents, lovers and employers,
until they cease being passive, masochistic or martyrlike. In
some cases, Wolpe claims, masochistic patients who failed
to improve in years of psychoanalysis changed radically in a
few weeks or months of assertive conditioning.

With five to ten percent of his patients, Wolpe uses sexual
excitement as the counterforce to anxiety—where sexual
intercourse itself is the situation producing the anxiety. The
desensitizing procedure is carried on privately by the patient,
outside the office. In a case involving an impotent man, for
instance, the couple is advised to engage patiently in prelimi-
nary sexplay with the understanding that intercourse will be
postponed until much later. With the major source of worry
about success or failure thus removed, the patient's pleasurable feelings can successfully overcome and inhibit the minor
anxiety of preliminaries; deconditioning proceeds until con-
summation itself causes little anxiety.

Aversive therapy—in which unpleasant experiences (the
electric shock used on the homosexual patient) are linked
with some undesirable neurotic act or habit to make the act
or habit itself become repellent—was given much attention
in the 1940s in connection with the treatment of alcoholism.
The usual technique was to give the patient an injection of a
nausea-inducing drug (such as apomorphine) and then offer
him his favorite alcoholic drink shortly before the onset of
the nausea. The intent was to make the very thought or sight

of a drink revolting. For unknown reasons, the results were inconsistent and impermanent, but in at least one follow-up study, about half of a large group of patients so treated were said to be abstinent two to five years later.

Behavior therapists are intrigued by aversive conditioning even though they have more failures or relapses with it than with other forms of conditioning therapy. Smoking, drug addiction, infidelity, as well as homosexuality, have been tackled by shooting electric current into the willing victim as he thinks of his undesirable activity; thus far, the claimed cures have all too often been followed by later relapses. Wolpe nonetheless continues to predict a significant place for aversion techniques in the armamentarium of behavior therapy.

The evaluation of the results of psychotherapy is probably less reliable than evaluations in any other form of treatment of human ailments. This is as true of the reports published by Freudians as of the reports by the behavior therapists. Few therapists of any school have made comprehensive long-term follow-ups of their patients; almost none have had independent outsiders rate their patients before and after treatment; almost none have used untreated control groups for comparison.

Bearing these caveats in mind, let us see what the behavior therapists say about their own results. Wolpe, in his own 1958 opus, *Psychotherapy by Reciprocal Inhibition,* summarizes nine years of his own practice: He states that 89.5 percent of his 210 patients were cured or much improved, the mean time in treatment being only about 30 therapeutic sessions. Since then Arnold Lazarus, now a colleague of Wolpe's at Temple University, has reported his own results with a series of 408 patients treated by behavior therapy: 78 percent, he says, derived marked benefit.

Wolpe and Lazarus in a recent coauthored manual (*Behavior Therapy Techniques*) compare their own cure-or-improvement rates of 89.5 percent and 78 percent with the rates given (in two classic studies) for psychoanalytic therapy —60 to 63.2 percent for patients treated anywhere from half a year to several years. If the comparisons are sound, behavior therapy is strikingly more effective, quicker and cheaper.

If the comparisons are sound—that is the key phrase. Wolpe and Lazarus, like the psychoanalysts whose results are summarized in the two classic studies, judged the illness and the degree of recovery in their patients by themselves; the possibilities of unwitting bias make any direct comparisons of the figures unscientific and unreliable. For that matter, the criteria used both by the behavior therapists and by the psychoanalysts are practically unquantifiable. What, exactly, does—to use the phrases in these studies—"improved interpersonal relationships" mean, and just how improved must a relationship be to rate the appraisal "major improvement"?

Psychotherapists also question Wolpe's reported results on other grounds. Some point out that he has not treated a carefully randomized sample of patients but an unselected group of adventitious referrals, most of which came from general practitioners; this may mean that his patients are unrepresentative of neurotics in general. Still others say that even though Wolpe's results may be genuine, they are due not to his hypothesized mechanism of reciprocal inhibition but to the classic mechanisms of transference, suggestion, direction, and so on.

This last point is the one Wolpe most energetically denies, since he considers his methods not only important in themselves but a crushing disproof of the Freudian theory of neurosis. "If freedom from symptoms is almost invariably lasting when procured without the use of analytic methods," he writes, "painful unconscious conflicts are almost certainly not the fountainhead of neurotic symptoms."

Yet it may be that in the future the two viewpoints will prove to be reconcilable. A few Freudian psychologists have begun to translate classic psychoanalysis into the terms of learning theory—considering the experiences of Freudian therapy, for instance, as a form of corrective deconditioning and reconditioning. At the same time, some behavior therapists find their own work turning up evidence of that selfsame unconscious whose existence Wolpe doubts. Joseph Cautela, for instance, a psychologist at Boston College, recently published a paper pointing out that several patients to whom he was giving behavior therapy spontaneously made emotionally insightful statements about themselves as they became desensitized; to a Freudian, these insights are much like those that emerge when a patient is undergoing orthodox psychotherapy.

Nonetheless, at present there is open hostility between the mavericks and the establishment—as was true in the case of Freud and his followers and the medical profession long ago. But not every maverick is a Freud, not every boy with a slingshot is a David. We shall have to watch the pebble in flight and see.

BIBLIOGRAPHY

Ballew, J. W., and Masters, W. H.   Mumps: A Cause of Infertility. I. Present Considerations. *Fertil. & Steril.* 5:536-543, 1954.

Bauer, J. D.; Ackerman, P. G., and Toro, G.   *Bray's Clinical Laboratory Methods* (7th ed.). St. Louis: The C. V. Mosby Co. 1968.

Goldhar, A.; Grody, M. H., and Masters, W. H.   The Vaginal Smear As an Ovulatory Index. *Fertil. & Steril.* 3:376-392, 1952.

Grody, M. H.; Robinson, D. W., and Masters, W. H.   The Cervical Cap: An Adjunct in the Treatment of Male Infertility. *J.A.M.A.* 149:427-431, 1952.

Johnson, V. E., and Masters, W. H.   Treatment of the Sexually Incompatible Family Unit. *Minn. Med.* 44:466-471, 1961.

Johnson, V. E., and Masters, W. H.   Intravaginal Contraceptive Study. Phase I. Anatomy. *West. J. Surg., Obst. & Gynec.* 70:202-207, 1962.

Johnson, V. E., and Masters, W. H. Intravaginal Contraceptive Study. Phase II. Physiology (A Direct Test for Protective Potential). *West. J. Surg., Obst. & Gynec.* 71:144-153, 1963.

Johnson, V. E.; Masters, W. H., and Lewis, K. C. The Physiology of Intravaginal Contraceptive Failure. In *Manual of Contraceptive Practice* (Calderone, M. S., Ed.). 6:138-150. Baltimore: The Williams & Wilkins Co., 1964.

Johnson, V. E., and Masters, W. H. Sexual Incompatibility: Diagnosis and Treatment. In *Human Reproduction and Sexual Behavior* (Lloyd, C. W., Ed.). 26:474-489. Philadelphia: Lea & Febiger, 1964.

Johnson, V. E., and Masters, W. H. A Team Approach to the Rapid Diagnosis and Treatment of Sexual Incompatibility. *Pac. Med. & Surg.* 72:371-375, 1964.

Johnson, V. E., and Masters, W. H. A Product of Dual Import: Intravaginal Infection Control and Conception Control. *Pac. Med. & Surg.* 73:267-271, 1965.

Lampe, E. H., and Masters, W. H. Problems of Male Fertility. II. Effect of Frequent Ejaculation. *Fertil. & Steril.* 7:123-127, 1956.

Masters, W. H. The Infertile Couple. A Basic Evaluation Technique. *J. Okla. S.M.A.* 49:517-521, 1956.

Masters, W. H. Infertility—A Family Unit Problem. *Minn. Med.* 40:842-846, 1957.

Masters, W. H. Infertility—A Family Unit Problem. *Medical Times* 86:825-832, 1958.

Masters, W. H. The Infertile Male—An Obstetrical Problem. *S. Dak. J. Med. & Pharm.* 12:131-134, 1959.

Masters, W. H. The Sexual Response Cycle of the Human Female: Vaginal Lubrication. *Ann. N. Y. Acad. Sci.* 83:301-317, 1959.

Masters, W. H. The Sexual Response Cycle of the Human Female: I. Gross Anatomic Considerations. *West. J. Surg., Obst. & Gynec.* 68:57-72, 1960.

Masters, W. H. Influence of Male Ejaculate on Vaginal Acidity. *Endocrine Dysfunction and Infertility* (report of the 35th Ross Conference on Pediatric Research). 76-78, 1960.

Masters, W. H. Clinical Significance of the Study of Human Sexual Response. *Medical Aspects of Human Sexuality.* 1:14-20, 1967.

Masters, W. H.; Grody, M. H., and Robinson, D. W. Management and Treatment of Infertility. *J.M.S.M.A.* 49:327-337, 1952.

Masters, W. H., and Johnson, V. E. The Human Female: Anatomy of Sexual Response. *Minn. Med.* 43:31-36, 1960.

Masters, W. H., and Johnson, V. E. Orgasm, Anatomy of the Female. In *The Encyclopedia of Sexual Behavior,* vol. 2 (Ellis, A., and Abarbanel, A., Eds.). 788-793. New York: Hawthorn Books, Inc., 1961.

Masters, W. H., and Johnson, V. E. The Physiology of the Vaginal Reproductive Function. *West. J. Surg., Obst. & Gynec.* 69:105-120, 1961.

Masters, W. H., and Johnson, V. E. The Artificial Vagina: Anatomic, Physiologic, Psychosexual Function. *West. J. Surg., Obst. & Gynec.* 69:192-212, 1961.

Masters, W. H., and Johnson, V. E. Intravaginal Environment. I. A Lethal Factor. *Fertil. & Steril.* 12:560-580, 1961.

Masters, W. H., and Johnson, V. E. The Sexual Response Cycle of the Human Female. III. The Clitoris: Anatomic and Clinical Considerations. *West. J. Surg., Obst. & Gynec.* 70:248-257, 1962.

Masters, W. H., and Johnson, V. E. The Sexual Response

Cycle of the Human Male. I. Gross Anatomic Considerations. *West. J. Surg., Obst. & Gynec.* 71:85-95, 1963.

Masters, W. H., and Johnson, V. E. The Clitoris: An Anatomic Baseline for Behavioral Investigation. In *Determinants of Human Sexual Behavior* (Winokur, G. W., Ed.). 3:44-51. Springfield, Ill.: Charles C. Thomas, 1963.

Masters, W. H., and Johnson, V. E. Sexual Response. Part II. Anatomy and Physiology. In *Human Reproduction and Sexual Behavior* (Lloyd, C. W., Ed.). 25:460-472. Philadelphia: Lea & Febiger, 1964.

Masters, W. H., and Johnson, V. E. Counseling with Sexually Incompatible Marriage Partners. In *Counseling in Marital and Sexual Problems: A Physician's Handbook* (Klemer, R. H., Ed.). 13:126-137. Baltimore: The Williams & Wilkins Co., 1965.

Masters, W. H., and Johnson, V. E. The Sexual Response Cycle of the Human Female. I. Gross Anatomic Considerations. In *Sex Research: New Developments* (Money, J., Ed.). 3:53-89. New York: Holt, Rinehart & Winston, Inc., 1965.

Masters, W. H., and Johnson, V. E. The Sexual Response Cycle of the Human Female. II. The Clitoris: Anatomic and Clinical Considerations. In *Sex Research: New Developments* (Money, J., Ed.). 4:90-112. New York: Holt, Rinehart & Winston, Inc., 1965.

Masters, W. H., and Johnson, V. E. The Sexual Response Cycles of the Human Male and Female: Comparative Anatomy and Physiology. In *Sex and Behavior* (Beach, F. A., Ed.). 25:512-534. New York: John Wiley & Sons, Inc., 1965.

Masters, W. H., and Johnson, V. E. *Human Sexual Response*. Boston: Little, Brown and Co., 1966.

Masters, W. H., and Johnson, V. E. Clinical Parameters of Human Reproduction and Sexual Behavior. In *Perspectives in Reproduction and Sexual Behavior* (Diamond, M., Ed.). Indiana University Press. In print.

Masters, W. H., and Johnson, V. E. The Scientist and His Interpreters. In *Bull. Am. Med. Writers Assoc.* (Dailey, E. G., Ed.). Vol. 17, no. 5, pp. 4-9, 1967.

Masters, W. H., and Johnson, V. E. Human Sexual Response: The Aging Female and the Aging Male. In *Middle Age and Aging* (Neugarten, B. L., Ed.). 30:269-279. Chicago and London: University of Chicago Press, 1968.

Masters, W. H.; Magallon, D. T., and Grody, M. H. Gonadotrophin Titer in the Adult Human Male: The Effect of Ejaculation. *J. Urol.* 67:1028-1036, 1952.

Masters, W. H.; Maze, L. E., and Gilpatrick, T. S. Etiological Approach to Habitual Abortion. *Am. J. Obst. & Gynec.* 73:1022-1032, 1957.

Masters, W. H.; Toro, G.; Ackerman, P. G., and Johnson, V. E. Biochemistry of Human Vaginal Lubrication. 1. Enzymology. *J. Fertil. & Steril.* In print. 1968.

Riley, F. J., and Masters, W. H. Problems of Male Fertility. III. Bacteriology of Human Semen. *Fertil. & Steril.* 7:128-132, 1956.